Black Walnut as a Crop

U.S. Forest Service
U.S. Department of Agriculture

University Press of the Pacific
Honolulu, Hawaii

Black Walnut as a Crop

by
U.S. Forest Service
U.S. Department of Agriculture

ISBN: 1-4102-2293-4

Reprinted from the 1975 edition

University Press of the Pacific
Honolulu, Hawaii
http://www.universitypressofthepacific.com

FOREWORD

The North Central Forest Experiment Station and the Northeastern Area, State & Private Forestry of the Forest Service appreciate the opportunity to join with Southern Illinois University and the Walnut Council in sponsoring this second symposium on the culture and use of black walnut. Active participants include members of the walnut industry and private landowners as well as scientists and specialists from various universities and State and Federal agencies. What these resourceful people have accomplished in a relatively short time says it all — cooperation pays off.

Southern Illinois University's contribution to walnut research and extension goes far beyond hosting the 1966 and 1973 Symposia. Through its School of Agriculture and Department of Forestry, the University has taken an active part in developing our cooperative research program by contributing space, funds, and scientific expertise. We know these contributions will pay big dividends for many years to come.

One of the primary objectives of the Walnut Council is to extend knowledge on how to tend and utilize black walnut trees. Its co-sponsorship of the symposium and its financial assistance in the publication of the proceedings are proof of the Council's interest and enthusiasm.

The papers in these proceedings clearly demonstrate that the state of the art and science of walnut culture has advanced considerably since the first Walnut Symposium in 1966, but they also indicate that a number of serious or potentially serious problems remain to be solved. Obviously, we can do more to increase the growing stock, to speed up growth, and to improve quality and utilization. We must not let up in our effort to learn more about walnut culture and to apply what we learn.

JOHN H. OHMAN, *Director*
North Central Forest Experiment Station
ROBERT D. RAISCH, *Director*
Northeastern Area, State & Private Forestry

BLACK WALNUT AS A CROP,
Black Walnut Symposium, Carbondale, Illinois, August 14-15, 1973

CONTENTS

CONTENTS, Continued

CONTENTS, Continued

● ● ● ● ●

PROGRESS THROUGH COOPERATION

John R. McGuire, *Chief*
USDA Forest Service
Washington, D.C.

I welcome the opportunity to meet with you on this beautiful campus. We share a deep interest in finding better ways to grow and utilize black walnut and other fine hardwoods.

Seven years ago, at the first Black Walnut Workshop, former Chief Ed Cliff, Dr. Delyte Morris, then president of Southern Illinois University, leaders in the fine hardwoods industry, and several hundred staunch supporters of black walnut dedicated the Tree Improvement Center here at Carbondale. Those of you who were present will recall that the area consisted of 40 acres of School of Agriculture pastureland and a few dozen newly planted walnut trees. Now the area contains excellent facilities for tree improvement research, all developed through the direct assistance of Southern Illinois University.

I would like to stress that the Tree Improvement Center and our new Forestry Sciences Laboratory were made possible through the support and cooperation of a great number of people. In fact, the walnut research and development program would not exist at all if it were not for a strong cooperative spirit. Various State, Federal, private organizations, and universities are working with hundreds of private landowners who have freely given of their land, their trees, and their time. This cooperative effort was further strengthened in 1970 with formation of the Walnut Council.

My sincerest congratulations to all of you for showing how effectively a grass roots movement can identify and vigorously pursue solutions to problems in resource management, especially as they apply to private lands. We in the Forest Service are proud to be a part of this program.

As many of you know, the Forest Service recently completed another review of our timber resources. The total hardwood situation has changed little from that shown in the 1962 Timber Trends Study. The 1970 volume growth exceeded drain, but high-quality logs are in short supply and the long-range outlook is not bright. Most of you know better than I that the prospect for quality walnut is bleak. In view of the intense pressure on the walnut resource during the past 10 to 15 years, I was amazed to see how much walnut growing stock still is present. This is evidence of the high value landowners place on both young and old walnut trees.

We are well aware that short supplies of veneer and saw logs are a critical problem for industry. Continuing strong export demands have further depleted the available supply and created difficult times for our domestic primary processors. Some of them have not survived the "crunch." Although the grower has benefited from the constantly rising prices for his trees, this trend is not without hazard. Walnut can more than hold its own on technical merits in competition with other woods and substitutes, but there are limits to what people will pay for genuine walnut products. If this beautiful wood is to retain its traditional place in a highly competitive market, it is obvious that we must find more efficient ways to grow and process walnut.

Considerable progress has been made toward finding solutions to some urgent problems. I am impressed that a lot of good research is being carried on at a number of locations. The papers presented during this symposium provide excellent summaries of what is now known about growing, harvesting, and utilizing black walnut for wood products and nuts. We should not fail to stress another desirable attribute of walnut trees, their esthetic value. Walnuts, especially open-grown trees, are an important part of the scenic beauty of the central hardwood region, both in summer and winter.

During the last Walnut Workshop, various speakers suggested that improvements in survival, growth, and quality were possible if certain practices were followed. In this meeting, you will learn that many of these early predictions were correct.

Perhaps the greatest progress in the past 7 years has been made in the field of extension. Research results are now made available promptly, so little time is lost in getting improved techniques into practices. This has been a team effort, and you should be proud of the results.

Communication between research and extension personnel has been excellent. I'm sure that this is partly because the Forest Service staff at Carbondale includes a well-qualified specialist from our Division of State and Private Forestry. This has resulted in close liaison with the State Divisions of Forestry and State and industry extension staffs. High landowner interest in obtaining planting stock and participating in cost-sharing programs shows that the linkage between extension and the walnut growers is bearing fruit.

Last spring I received a copy of the February issue of *Plywood and Panel* from the publisher, Mr. James Burrell. The cover picture and the story about Bob Hollowell's walnut plantings near Martinsville, Indiana, show what can be done by a private landowner. The story describes a very successful large walnut plantation that is used by both research and extension to test and demonstrate management practices. Natural walnut trees on the same farm receive necessary release and pruning. Other companies and individuals are making similar intensive efforts to establish and grow walnut following the best advice they can get. You have a good story, and you need to tell it again and again.

We are making good progress, but we have a long way to go in solving all the urgent problems in walnut culture and use. For example, we know that intensive culture of any crop can create conditions favorable to insect and disease attacks. Much needs to be learned about the pests involved, their potential impact on growth and value, and the control measures that will be effective. Without this information, the landowner might lose his investment in walnut plantations or become so discouraged that he would stop trying to grow walnuts. Future supplies for industry would suffer.

We also need reliable data to determine the economics of growing walnut for wood and nut crops on both good and poor sites. Some individual landowners are trying unique multicropping systems — producing crops of grass, hay, or small grains between the trees in their young walnut plantations. Suitable techniques will have to be developed that minimize potential animal damage to the trees. We need to capitalize on such opportunities to improve income on farm operations.

2

The success or failure of our program to increase production of walnut and other fine hardwoods will depend on the degree of participation by nonindustry private landowners who own 75 percent of the hardwood sawtimber. Their land includes most of the productive walnut sites and nearly all the walnut growing stock. We need to stimulate greater interest among the small private landowners in developing maximum productivity of their forest lands. A good research and extension program will help, but experience has shown that direct incentives also can be reached.

Past and present cooperative forestry programs, such as the Civilian Conservation Corps, Prairie States Forestry Project, Cooperative Forest Management, Soil Bank, and the Rural Environmental Assistance Program, have resulted in the establishment of more than 35 million acres of plantations. I'm sure much of this progress would not have been made without these programs.

We know that use of intensive practices such as thinning and pruning can greatly increase walnut growth and quality. We also know that once a landowner begins to follow such practices he is apt to develop a continuing interest and pride in keeping his woodland productive. These are good arguments for a program to encourage planting more walnut and other fine hardwoods and applying cultural practices when they are needed.

The Forest Service is developing a financial incentives program for small woodland owners to assist them in improving productivity of their forest land. We feel this approach is a viable one for promoting good management practices on small ownerships. The small nonindustrial owner needs both financial and technical help.

Record prices for walnut have led to some vexing situations. I would like to challenge the Walnut Council and all of you attending this symposium to do something about two urgent problems. First, we need to convince landowners that they should not sell walnut trees just because they have reached minimum merchantable size, because the volume being added to such trees will produce the greatest rate of return. Second, we need to allay the fears of landowners who may consider selling their trees prematurely — before they are stolen. The actual volume of stolen trees is relatively small, but the wide press coverage given "tree rustling" surely has a detrimental influence on the landowner's decision. Prospective tree planters or those with trees needing release, thinning, or pruning might well become so discouraged about potential theft that they would hesitate to invest in walnut culture.

Although many problems remain to be solved, you can all be proud of what has been accomplished in this cooperative program. I hope you will take advantage of the momentum you have generated in walnut and expand this interest to include other fine hardwoods on small private forest holdings. How well these lands are managed will largely determine the role of fine hardwoods in meeting future needs for timber and in making our Nation a more attractive place to live.

SEVEN YEARS OF GROWTH

Gene W. Grey, *Assistant State Forester*
Kansas State University
Manhattan, Kansas

ABSTRACT.—The 7 years since the Black Walnut Workshop have shown a continued decline in walnut log quality. The application of new research, tree improvement programs, and intensive culture give hope, however, that this downward curve may soon flatten. The walnut industry must also address itself to problems of marketing, economics, seedling production, and even social areas.

In August of 1966, a landmark walnut workshop was held here at Southern Illinois University. Jointly sponsored by the USDA Forest Service, the American Walnut Manufacturers Association, and Southern Illinois University, the workshop was born of a genuine concern to improve the quality of the black walnut resource. Edward Cliff,[1] then Chief of the Forest Service, clearly expressed this concern in his keynote speech: "Efforts to improve supplies of quality timber in America are long overdue. The over-all quality of our hardwood timber resources has been in a long decline as we harvested the best trees of the most desirable species and left the poorest to grow and reproduce. We have at last reversed the downward trend in volume — now that growth exceeds cut — but we have a long uphill fight to improve the quality of the timber we grow — especially in the hardwood species."

Now, we are gathered here again, 7 years later, to see how far up the hill we have come, and how far we have yet to go. The objective of this symposium is to summarize the state of the art concerning walnut, to present relevant new information, and to identify what else needs to be done. To set the stage, perhaps it would be well to briefly review some significant happenings since the 1966 workshop, to illustrate some of our successes, and to identify, alas, some of our shortcomings.

The 1966 workshop was certainly not the beginning of black walnut in the nation. It was, rather, perhaps a

logical development growing out of all that had gone before. It did, however, focus attention on the species as nothing before had ever done, and thus must be regarded as an important landmark.

The challenge from that workshop — to reverse the downward trend in quality — has not yet been met. The walnut veneer and furniture industry is utilizing materials today that are of generally lower quality than 7 years ago. I quote Donald Gott of the Fine Hardwoods American Walnut Association, who after receiving opinions from a cross section of their membership said: "I am sorry to report the situation universally is severe from the standpoint of declining quality, and a continuation of a downward curve is quite evident."

So we can only hope that the curve may soon begin to flatten. A look at some of the happenings in walnut during the past 7 years gives reason for this hope:

The Building of a Solid, Relevant Research Base.— In the early 1960's, the USDA Forest Service made a commitment to an intensive effort in walnut research. This commitment was manifested in the development of the walnut research center here at Carbondale, related work at the Forest Products Laboratory, and the underwriting of numerous projects at universities within the species range. There has also been a significant input from other public and private organizations. We have confirmed some of what we thought, we have exploded some myths, and we have made some new discoveries. Most importantly, however, we have armed our field foresters with an accurate body of knowledge.

The Application of Research Findings.—While this happening spreads itself over others that I will discuss

---

[1] *Edward P. Cliff. The increasing challenge of decreasing quality. In Black walnut culture, USDA For. Serv., North Cent. For. Exp. Stn., St. Paul, Minn., p. 1-3. 1966.*

later, it is significant unto itself, as application is not always the result of research in forestry.

The Initiation of Walnut Tree Improvement Programs. —Three States have developed improved walnut seed-production areas and are collecting seed from them. Nine others have seed orchards not yet in significant production. Superior trees have been located and propagated across the species range. Materials are being exchanged and testing is underway.

The Intensive Culture of Existing Walnut Trees. — Perhaps no other species in the history of American forestry has been as intensively managed as walnut. In our native woodlands, we are concentrating more on single trees than on stands. If we have not developed a totally new silvicultural system, we have modified the traditional one nearly beyond recognition.

The Creation of the Walnut Council. —The Walnut Council was born on September 1, 1970. This birth was the result of the conception some 9 months earlier at a tree improvement meeting in Hannibal, Missouri. The details of this conception and birth are available upon request. The general objectives of the Council are to advance knowledge of the culture of walnut species, to encourage the planting of walnut, to encourage the management of naturally established walnut, and to perpetuate the utilization of all walnut products. The only qualification for membership is an interest in walnut. We now have over 562 members representing 27 States and three foreign countries.

If we are to be objective, however, we must recognize our problems as well as our successes. It is in the spirit of constructive criticism that I offer the following comments as to our problems and areas of disagreement:

Marketing. —We are the forest industry with maximum confusion in the market place. Universal or regional log-grade standards are not used, and log-value information is not readily available to the seller. This confusion manifests itself in the criticism by service foresters of the industry's log-purchasing system, and conversely, the criticism by the industry of foresters who give log-value estimates to landowners. We skirt the edges of this problem, and seem afraid to meet it head-on. But, I believe we must, and I will recommend this as a priority item for the appropriate committees of the Walnut Council.

Economics. —Our knowledge of black walnut economics is weak. Even weaker is our application of the

economic knowledge we do have. The increased emphasis on walnut management in recent years is predicated on little more than an assumption that walnut is valuable and always will remain so. Foresters are recommending and landowners are carrying out cultural practices with only a vague understanding of the economic consequences of their actions.

Monoculture. —We have been criticized for concentrating on walnut at the expense of other hardwoods. This question has been raised most often from the standpoint of priorities for research monies. Another question seems appropriate, too: Are we practicing discriminatory silviculture in the woods, and might we not pay a high price for this in the long run? I have no answer here, but I have seen excellent sycamore, hackberry, and other species cut or girdled to release walnut in my own State. If this is the case throughout the species range, perhaps there is valid cause for concern.

Chemicals. —The uncontrolled use of herbicides and other chemicals is a very real threat to the walnut resource. In my own State, at the western edge of the walnut range, aerial application of herbicides in the name of pasture improvement and range conservation is widespread. In some counties it is virtually impossible to find walnut trees undamaged by 2,4-D or 2,4,5-T. Because of the mass application of these herbicides, grapes are no longer grown commercially in Kansas and portions of other States. That this could happen to walnut, too, cannot be shrugged off as another unfounded forecast of doom.

Seedling Production. —Production and distribution of black walnut seedlings has fluctuated greatly since 1966. Williams and Phares[2] reported that the State nurseries distributed 1.7 million walnut seedlings in 1966. This dropped to 1.4 million in 1967, and since has climbed to 2.7 million in 1971. State nursery distribution of stratified nuts has shown a similar pattern:

Year	Seedlings	Stratified Nuts	Total
1966	1,673,420	536,411	2,209,831
1967	1,372,605	486,195	1,858,800
1968	2,377,669	433,124	2,810,793
1969	2,266,284	494,593	2,760,877
1970	2,532,646	451,900	2,984,546
1971	2,701,647	875,524	3,577,171

[2] *Robert D. Williams, and Robert E. Phares. Black walnut seedling production and related nursery research. Northeast. Area Nurserymen's Proc. (In press.)*

These figures are open to interpretation. My interpretation points to two related problems: (1) *Seed scarcity.* — Most States reported an inability to meet their production demands because of seed scarcity, particularly in 1970 and 1971. This scarcity was compounded by competition from the nut industry. The obvious question here is: Can we not provide nut storage so that we do not always have to depend on this year's nut crop for next year's seedlings? Surely the cost of storage is far less than the cost of not having seedlings. (2) *Technical assistance.* — On-the-ground technical assistance must accompany walnut planting programs in order to obtain quantity and quality. There has not been a significant increase in public or private service forestry positions in the field since 1966. And there have been increasing demands on the field forester's time from other facets of forest management. In short, we have superimposed the job of walnut planting and culture on an existing organization without provision for expansion.

Exports. — The export of walnut veneer logs continues, and we are not much closer to a solution, or even agreement among ourselves, than we were 7 years ago. Exports have exceeded domestic consumption since 1967, and there is no export control program. Exports, however, have dropped from a high of 22 million board feet in 1968 to 13 million feet in 1971. Domestic consumption has declined also.

The Small Woodland Owner. — The key to the future of black walnut is the small woodland owner. He owns most of the resource, and whatever influences him influences the resource. His pressures are many — taxes, pollution, urbanization, and competition from the many other facets of our society. If we are to secure the future of walnut, we must continue to make walnut growing competitive with other land-use alternatives. But if we are to be truly successful, we must also come out of the woods and work to modify the other facets of our society that influence the woodland owner, and consequently the walnut resource.

In summary, I believe we have built a solid technical base for growing walnut. We know what to do. We are not doing it enough. We must also address ourselves to the problems of marketing, economics, and related aspects of our society. Perhaps then we can truly begin the long climb up the hill of quality.

TIMBER DEMAND AND USE

James E. Blyth, *Principal Market Analyst*
North Central Forest Experiment Station
St. Paul, Minnesota

ABSTRACT.—The use of walnut increased from 1933 to the mid-1960's, then probably peaked out between 1963 and 1968. The proportion of walnut logs used for veneer has been increasing during the last two decades while the proportion used for lumber has been declining. Most export logs are cut into veneer. The demand for walnut logs has varied considerably during the 1960's, but the general trend of log prices has been sharply upward. Rising prices with fluctuating demand indicate a scarcity of high-quality walnut, a need for more efficient and complete utilization of the walnut resource, and the necessity for reducing costs in domestic manufacturing of walnut products so they can remain competitive with substitutes and foreign products.

Records of the annual cut of walnut timber for all products are incomplete for recent years. However, the use of walnut increased from 1933 to the mid-1960's, then probably peaked out between 1963 and 1968. For the years in which a census of wood used in manufacturing was made, the quantity of walnut wood used for all products (including log exports) ranged from 29 million board feet in 1933 to 141 million board feet in 1965 (fig. 1). Although more than half of the walnut logs were manufactured into lumber in 1965, the proportion used for veneer increased significantly in the last two decades. Most export logs are cut into veneer.

SAW LOG DEMAND AND USE

Sawmills producing walnut lumber are scattered throughout the natural range of walnut. Most of these mills saw less than 100,000 board feet of walnut lumber annually, but a few saw more than 1,000,000 board feet per year and are often integrated with a hardwood veneer mill or specialize in walnut products such as gunstock blanks. Sawmills receiving large amounts of walnut logs often sort them into saw logs and veneer logs and in some instances further segregate the logs for domestic and export markets.

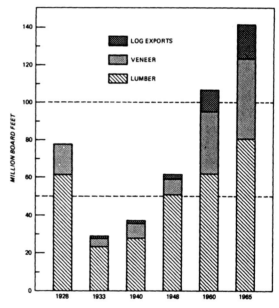

Figure 1. — *Walnut wood use in selected years, 1928-1965; log exports: Scribner Decimal C log rule. Source: Lumber used in manufacturing 1928, 1933, 1940; wood used in manufacturing 1948, 1960, 1965; U S D A Forest Service and U.S. Department of Commerce export statistics.*

From the sawmills, walnut lumber is shipped to furniture plants, other industrial plants, or overseas. In recent years, walnut lumber exports and their average value per thousand board feet have been:

Year	Lumber exports (Million bd. ft.)	Average value (Dollars per thousand bd. ft.)
1962	5.4	405
1963	5.3	435
1964	7.6	398
1965	7.5	371
1966	8.7	390
1967	5.2	469
1968	4.9	489
1969	6.4	462
1970	6.9	429
1971	3.1	563

Source: U.S. Bureau of Census Annual Report FT 410

Although 1971 lumber exports were at the lowest level in a decade, the average value was the highest for that period.

Leading walnut lumber-producing States include Indiana, Missouri, Kansas, Ohio, Iowa, Kentucky, Illinois, West Virginia, and Tennessee. The censuses of wood used in manufacturing indicate that lumber use in manufacturing increased from 24 million board feet in 1933 to 80 million board feet in 1965.

A 1966 walnut logging utilization study in Indiana showed that 83 percent of the volume of saw logs harvested was growing stock[1] and 17 percent was nongrowing stock.[2] The saw log volume cut from nongrowing stock included 73 percent from trees on nonforest land, 16 percent from cull trees and cull sections, and 11 percent from limbwood. In addition, this study estimated that 19 percent of the walnut growing stock cut during saw log harvesting was left in the woods as residue. Based upon this study, a significant quantity of growing stock is not used, while nongrowing stock is apparently an important source of walnut saw logs.

---

[1] Growing stock volume – net volume in cubic feet of sound wood in the boles of live sawtimber and poletimber trees from stump to a minimum 4.0-inch top diameter outside bark of the central stem or to the point where the central stem breaks into limbs. Short-log trees are not included.

[2] Nongrowing stock – limbwood, saplings, cull trees, cull sections of growing stock trees, dead trees, and trees on nonforest and noncommercial forest land.

VENEER LOG DEMAND AND USE

Consumption of walnut veneer logs has varied greatly since 1961, depending upon domestic housing and furniture market strength, worldwide business conditions, and export regulations (table 1). At the same time, the average value has doubled for veneer logs purchased and export logs — an indication that high-quality logs are becoming scarce.

Walnut veneer log harvesting for domestic mills is concentrated in the North-Central Region[3] with significant quantities coming from the Northeast[4] and minor quantities from the South (fig. 2). The 1963 and 1968 harvest of walnut veneer logs for domestic use in selected States was:

State	Quantity (Million bd. ft.)	
	1968	1963
Illinois	3.0	2.3
Indiana	7.4	6.7
Iowa	3.4	4.5
Kansas	.9	4.5
Kentucky	2.6	2.7
Michigan	.5	1.2
Minnesota	.3	.3
Missouri	2.3	2.5
Nebraska	.2	.4
Ohio	2.2	4.2
Tennessee	.1	1.5
West Virginia	.6	.7
Wisconsin	.8	.4

Sources: USDA Forest Service Research Note WO-6, Resource Bulletins NC-10, NE-21, and SO-25; unpublished data from North Central and Northeastern Forest Experiment Stations, USDA Forest Service.

Indiana supplied nearly 300 out of every thousand board feet of veneer logs required by domestic mills in 1968. Many veneer mills, using large quantities of walnut, are concentrated in Indiana and nearby States.

---

[3] Includes Indiana, Illinois, Iowa, Missouri, Kansas, Nebraska, Michigan, Wisconsin, Minnesota, North Dakota, and South Dakota.

[4] Includes Ohio, Kentucky, West Virginia, Maryland, Pennsylvania, New York, Massachusetts, Connecticut, Delaware, Rhode Island, Vermont, Maine, New Hampshire, and New Jersey.

Table 1. — *Walnut veneer log consumption, exports, and average value for selected years, 1961-1972.*

Year	Domestic consumption	Average value of: logs acquired per MBF	Quantity exported	Average value of: exports per MBF	Total consumption[2/]
	Million bd. ft.[1/]	Dollars per thousand bd. ft.	Million bd. ft.[1/]	Dollars per thousand bd. ft.	Million bd. ft.[1/]
1961	17.8	531	7.2	824	25.0
1962	22.4	586	10.3	961	32.7
1963	23.5	660	14.4	940	37.9
1964	19.8	719	9.6	1,105	29.4
1968	16.1	1,015	21.8	1,522	37.9
1969	12.4	1,108	20.8	1,519	33.2
1970	10.8	1,142	17.2	1,578	28.0
1971	10.2	1,167	12.9	1,666	23.1
1972	NA	NA	15.1	1,664	NA

1/ Scribner Dec. C log rule.
2/ Total consumption equals domestic consumption plus exports.
NA Not available.
Source: Office of Business Research and Analysis, Bureau of Domestic Commerce, U.S. Department of Commerce.

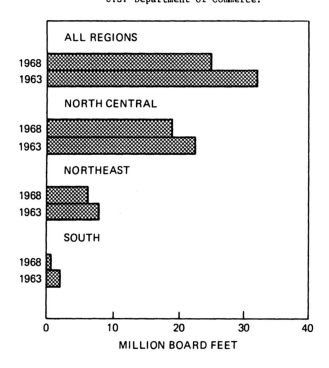

Figure 2. — *Walnut log harvest by region for domestic veneer mills, 1963 and 1968; International ¼-inch log rule. Source: USDA Forest Service Research Note WO-6, Resource Bulletins NC-10, NE-21, and SO-25.*

In 1971 our export log volume was shipped primarily to West Germany (36 percent of total), Japan (19 percent), Canada (11 percent), Italy (11 percent), Brazil (7 percent), and Switzerland (6 percent). Overall, European countries received 62 percent of the 1971 walnut log volume exported. In addition, the U.S. exported 97.7 million square feet (surface measure) of walnut veneer in 1971. The major importers of veneer were West Germany (66 percent of total) and Canada (27 percent).[5]

Some of our exports return as imports after processing. For example, in 1971 the U.S. imported 20.5 million square feet (surface measure) of walnut face plywood with a clear finish face; nearly all of it came from Japan.[6] Apparently the Japanese, using an efficient, relatively low-cost labor supply, are continuing to compete effectively with our veneer and plywood industry.

SUMMARY

Overall, the demand for walnut logs has varied considerably during the 1960's, but the general trend of log prices has been sharply upward. Rising prices with fluctuating demand reflect a scarcity of high-quality walnut, a need for more efficient and complete utilization of the walnut resource, and the necessity for reducing costs in domestic manufacturing of walnut products so they can remain competitive with substitutes and foreign products.

[5] *Export data from U.S. Bureau of Census Annual Report FT 410, 1971.*

[6] *Import data from U.S. Bureau of Census Annual Report FT 246, 1971.*

CHANGING RESOURCE AND UTILIZATION

Glenn A. Cooper, *Principal Forest Products Technologist*
Eugene F. Landt, *Principal Forest Products Technologist*
Ronald D. Lindmark, *Principal Economist*
and
Harold A. Stewart, *Forest Products Technologist*

Forestry Sciences Laboratory[1]
North Central Forest Experiment Station
Carbondale, Illinois

ABSTRACT.—Recent studies show that although the high-quality black walnut supply is diminishing, much untapped material is still available. The trees growing on
nonforest land and logging residues can supply many of our needs. That low-quality
material can be utilized has been demonstrated by woods residue recovery and conver-
sion into products. Improved drying and machining techniques can increase efficiency
of high-quality dimension part production, especially from low-quality raw material.
Therefore, the manufacturer who practices close utilization can use the additional black
walnut sources profitably.

High-quality black walnut is scarce, and the annual
harvest continues to exceed the annual growth of high-
quality timber. However, recent studies have shown
that black walnut trees growing on nonforest land, and
leftover material that is below current size and quality
standards, add substantially to the overall black walnut
supply. How best to use this untapped resource is a
question facing the walnut industry.

Recent timber supply data indicate that more low-
grade black walnut could be marketed if collection and
processing of substandard size and grade material were
feasible. Research has shown that high-quality dimension parts can be produced from low-quality material.
The problem is not the quality of the wood, but the high
production costs entailed in extracting lower yields
and smaller pieces from the lower grade flitches and
lumber. Hopefully, the demand for black walnut can
offset higher production costs.

It appears that much low-value raw material could be
utilized if processing was more intensive. Dimension
processed from residue, improved machining of small
parts, and improved drying systems for small pieces
all promise to increase the yield of usable material.

---

[1] *The laboratory is maintained in cooperation with
Southern Illinois University.*

THE RESOURCE

Several improvements in surveying the black walnut
resource have been made since our last workshop 7
years ago.

The volume in short-log trees on commercial forest
land and the volume in merchantable trees on nonforest
land are now reported. However, because walnut is a
minor species in every State in which it grows, resource
data obtained by survey sampling are subject to wide
statistical variation.

The most recent national data on the black walnut
resource (USDA Forest Service 1972), released only
a few months ago, do not differ greatly from those published in 1965 (USDA Forest Service 1965). Both sets
of data account only for black walnut growing on commercial forest land.[2] The recent data indicate that black
walnut growing stock volume is just under 1 billion
cubic feet.[2] The geographic distribution of this resource
is shown in figure 1. More than half the walnut is located
in the central region, and an additional 35 percent is in
the adjoining States of Kansas, Tennessee, Pennsylvania, and the Virginias.

---

[2] *See glossary on page 15 for forest survey definitions.*

Figure 1. — *The percentage distribution of black walnut growing stock volume by geographic region, 1970.*

Since the previous surveys did not include short-log trees and completely ignored the resource on nonforest land, the more recent surveys have been designed to evaluate all sources of walnut.[2] One of the first surveys to evaluate wooded strips, fence rows, and pastures as sources of black walnut was conducted in Kentucky (Lindmark and DeBald 1969).

The Kentucky survey revealed that nonforest land and short-log trees added 33 percent to Kentucky's commercial forest resource. As expected, fewer than one-third of the open-grown, sawtimber-sized trees will yield a 16-foot log. About 25 percent had no usable bolt, and 11 percent contained only one 6- or 7-foot bolt.

The first State survey that included short-log trees on commercial forest land as well as the resource on nonforest land was done in Kansas (Chase and Strickler 1968). The short-log trees and growing stock on nonforest land added 41 percent to the growing stock volume and 25 percent to the sawtimber volume. Of the estimated 60 million cubic feet of walnut volume in Kansas, 9 million cubic feet were from nonforest land, and 9 million cubic feet were from short-log trees growing on commercial forest land. Approximately 83 percent of the total volume is considered merchantable. Total sawtimber volume approached 120 million board feet, of which almost two-thirds was in Grade 1 and 2 logs.

However, only 15 percent of the trees were larger than 19 inches in diameter.

The most recent resource survey in Indiana showed that black walnut growing stock remained relatively constant between 1950 and 1967 (Spencer 1969). Volume losses in the larger diameter classes were more than offset by gains in the smaller diameter groups. Thus, the total black walnut growing stock actually increased from 63 million cubic feet in 1950 to 65 million cubic feet in 1967. During this period sawtimber volume also increased slightly in the smaller diameter groups but decreased in diameter classes over 15 inches.

The resource not previously included in the Indiana survey — trees on nonforest land and those on commercial forest land containing only 8- to 11-foot saw logs — added 17 million cubic feet or 26 percent to the resource. A total of 41 million board feet was added to the sawtimber resource.

The various national and State surveys indicate that changes in black walnut growing stock volume have been slight. Some of these surveys have also determined that the black walnut growing on nonforest land adds a significant volume to our total walnut resource. Although the growth-cut comparisons for black walnut indicated a near balance in 1963, the annual cut of high-quality material exceeded growth by an estimated 47 percent (Quigley and Lindmark 1967). The more recent surveys also indicate that the volume of high-quality black walnut timber is declining. This is evidenced, in part, by a decline in the production of veneer logs in the Central States region (Blyth 1968, Ginnaty 1970, 1972). Along with this, there has been a noticeable increase in the price of walnut stumpage, although in Illinois prices have declined gradually from a peak reached early in 1972 (Illinois Cooperative Crop Reporting Service 1972, USDA Forest Service 1965).

How efficiently are we utilizing our walnut resource? A recent study in Indiana showed that for every 1,000 board feet of saw logs harvested, 182 cubic feet of black walnut timber were cut (Blyth *et al.* 1969). Of the volume utilized, 83 percent was from growing stock and the remaining 17 percent was from nongrowing stock, including limbwood, cull trees, and timber from nonforest land. Sixteen percent of the walnut cut was left in the woods as residue. The residue component included saw-log portions, upper stems, as well as cull tree material.

IMPROVING BLACK WALNUT UTILIZATION

Black walnut utilization is changing as the supply of high-quality wood declines. Utilization methods have been modified to convert smaller and shorter logs than was common 20 years ago. Veneer manufacturers have successfully changed to thinner veneers than were formerly made. Drying operations have been improved to reduce kiln degrade, and more care in all phases of secondary manufacture is the order of the day. However, to augment the supply of black walnut for furniture parts, we need effective methods of processing non-commercial, low-quality residue material. We must learn how to salvage logging residue and process dimension cuttings from unmerchantable short-tree sections, short logs, tops, and large branches.

Dimension from Residue

We made dimension parts from residue collected in southern Illinois to determine the yield and costs (Dunmire *et al.* 1972). The residue was bucked into 813 bolts 2 to 6½ feet in length and 5½ to 17 inches in diameter. The bolts were then live-sawed on a portable bolter saw into 1⅛-inch-thick rough flitches sawing through and through. Stacked flitches were air- and kiln-dried to 7 percent moisture content.

The bolts yielded about 75 percent of their International ¼-Inch Rule scaled volume in usable cuttings. If this percentage is based on the Doyle Rule, which is commonly used by the walnut industry, the yield values would be greater because the Doyle Rule scale volumes are about 50 percent lower than the International ¼-Inch Rule scale volumes for small diameter bolts. For all cutting lengths, recovery volumes of clear-one-side cuttings ranged from 85 percent of the International ¼-Inch Rule scale for clear bolts to 72 percent for bolts with no clear faces (table 1).

As expected, the cost of manufacturing dimension from residue is high. It took us from 1 to 4 hours of bolter saw time per thousand board feet, depending on bolt size. Subsequent rough milling required 8 to 23

Table 1. — *Average black walnut dimension yields including sapwood based on International ¼-Inch Scale by cutting length classes from bolts of various grades*

Bolt grade[1]	International 1/4-Inch Rule bolt scale[2]	Dimension cutting grade	Yield by dimension length classes			Average total yield of International 1/4-Inch Rule bolt scale volume[5]
			12-23[4]	24-47	48-78	
	Board feet		Percent of bolt volume			Percent
C-4F	341	C-2S[3]	19.5	47.0	16.8	83.3
		C-1S & Better	17.9	48.3	18.6	84.8
		CM & Better	16.1	49.9	19.0	85.0
C-3F	725	C-2S	22.8	41.1	13.2	77.1
		C-1S & Better	15.8	46.9	15.9	78.6
		CM & Better	15.6	46.7	17.2	79.5
C-2F	1,415	C-2S	22.0	36.7	12.7	71.4
		C-1S & Better	19.9	39.4	13.6	72.9
		CM & Better	17.6	41.1	15.4	74.1
C-1F	1,838	C-2S	25.2	37.2	10.4	72.8
		C-1S & Better	22.9	40.1	12.2	75.2
		CM & Better	21.8	40.1	14.2	76.1
C-0F	2,347	C-2S	29.7	32.9	7.2	69.8
		C-1S & Better	27.3	36.8	7.9	72.0
		CM & Better	28.5	36.0	9.6	74.1
Average for all bolt grades	6,666	C-2S	25.5	36.6	10.4	72.5
		C-1S & Better	22.9	39.9	11.7	74.5
		CM & Better	21.5	40.9	13.4	75.8

1/ "C" refers to Clear and "F" refers to Face (1/4 of the bolt surface full length).

2/ Doyle Scale volumes are about 50 percent less than the International 1/4-Inch Rule Scale volumes.

3/ "C" refers to Clear, "S" refers to a top or bottom surface of a cutting, and "CM" refers to Character Marked, which includes some sound defects.

4/ 12- to 23-inch class also includes cuttings 1- to 1-1/2 inches wide by all lengths.

5/ Percent yield values based on the Doyle scale are about double the percent yield values that are based on the International 1/4-Inch Scale (i.e., the average Doyle based yield value for C-1S & Better for all bolt grades would be about 150 percent).

hours per thousand board feet (Dunmire *et al.* 1972, USDA Forest Service 1971). However, this high cost is offset first by the high yields and prices of dimension, and second by the steadily increasing demand for walnut products. A comparison between the estimated gross dollar return for the highest-grade bolts and the lowest-grade bolts shown illustrates that even low-grade bolts can give a high return (fig. 2). This should encourage the ingenious operator to attempt closer utilization and thereby benefit from residue that would otherwise be wasted.

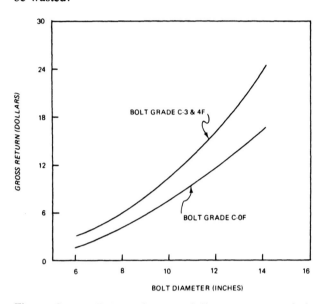

Figure 2. — *Estimated gross dollar return per bolt for clear-one-side (C-1S) 4/4-inch-thick flat dimension from grade C-3 and 4F and C-OF black walnut bolts 4 feet long. The gross return was determined for different bolt sizes by using an average estimated selling price of $1,000 per M board feet for the clear-one-side black walnut dimension with random widths and lengths.*

Walnut residue, when converted to dimension cuttings, is suitable for a variety of consumer products. Furniture parts, picture framing, decorative plaques, bowls, and even paneling have been made from small parts edge-glued and finger-jointed. An important finding was that the properties and appearance of black walnut dimension parts are the same whether the parts are made from conventional lumber or converted from residue. Attractive, high-quality products can be made from the cuttings (fig. 3).

Production of black walnut dimension from standard lumber has not been neglected. The Forest Products Laboratory in Madison, Wisconsin, developed charts for predicting dimension yields from the top four lumber grades (Shumann 1971). These yield data are valuable for furniture and dimension plant operators to use in grade selection, in determining grade mixes and costs, and for scheduling production time. With the charts it is possible to make yield and cost comparisons to achieve the greatest economy for a particular cutting order.

Dimension Drying

An important processing step in producing usable black walnut material for further manufacture is drying. The complex interactions of black walnut wood fiber, extractives, and water have been studied in depth to help develop better methods of drying and stabilizing the wood. It is well known that the extractives in black walnut stabilize the wood against shrinking and swelling as moisture content of the wood changes. We found that drying lowered the moisture content at fiber saturation from 48 percent to 31 percent, and extraction lowered it to 28 percent moisture content. This showed that the extractives had a greater affinity for water (hygroscopicity) than the cell walls, and thereby altered shrinking and swelling.[3] This means we can alter wood properties by changing the relationships between extractives and cell walls using physical or mechanical means.

Research has shown that freezing is one way to change the role of extractives in wood, and it greatly benefits drying of black walnut. Freshly cut black walnut (at about 80 percent moisture content) is not damaged by freezing because there is sufficient void space in the wood to accommodate the expansion of water to ice. Freezing and then thawing before drying, called prefreezing, increases the beneficial role extractives play during the drying process.

In studies of prefrozen black walnut, the drying behavior, shrinkage, strain and set development, moisture gradients and drying rate, drying defects, and changes in extractive availability were measured. When black walnut test specimens were frozen at six temperatures ranging from -10 to -320°F., shrinkage was reduced by prefreezing (Cooper *et al.* 1970). We found that induced shrinkage reduction and altered moisture affinity

---

[3]*G. A. Cooper. The effect of black walnut extractives on sorption, shrinkage, and swelling. Unpublished manuscript on file at North Cent. For. Exp. Stn., Carbondale, Ill. 1972.*

Figure 3. — *Small black walnut bolts produce high-quality dimension parts that are suitable for the manufacture of attractive products.*

resulted from the combined effects of prefreezing on increased extractives bulking and altered wood creep. The greatest effect was induced by prefreezing at -110 F.; storage time intervals after prefreezing did not affect shrinkage reductions (Cooper 1972). We also found that prefreezing of black walnut results in greater radial permeability of both the sapwood and heartwood.[4]

after prefreezing did not affect shrinkage reductions (Cooper 1972). We also found that prefreezing of black walnut results in greater radial permeability of both the sapwood and heartwood.[4]

These favorable responses to prefreezing indicate that we can improve the processing of dimension parts in several ways. First, because prefreezing increases permeability, the free water in wood can be dried out faster than without prefreezing. Second, increased permeability means we may be able to impregnate chemicals into prefrozen black walnut faster than into wood that has not been prefrozen. For example, stabilization with polyethylene glycol-1000 might be accomplished more readily if black walnut has been prefrozen. This is being investigated now. Third, because shrinkage is reduced, there are fewer shrinkage-related defects in prefrozen black walnut. Honeycomb and collapse are reduced significantly, particularly in thick stock. Prefreezing therefore holds promise for an improved drying system for high-value thick dimension, such as turning

squares and gunstocks, by decreasing drying time and drying defects.

Machining Improvements

One problem in processing black walnut dimension parts into panels is that the glued up panels will have a variation in slope of grain. This can cause surface machining defects, such as chipped grain. Therefore, to get the maximum yield from low-grade material, we need planing methods that minimize the amount of subsequent processing and waste. Machining research at Carbondale has shown that two methods of planing reduce planing defects and waste (Stewart 1970a, 1970b, 1971). The first, abrasive planing, eliminates the conventional knife planing defects and requires only about 0.010 and 0.015 inch of subsequent sanding to produce a satisfactory surface for finishing. However, the waste from abrasive planing is sanding dust; if uses for the dust are not found, there is a disposal problem.

The second method, cross-grain knife planing, can be applied to panels not longer than the width of the cabinet planers. This may be as much as 52 inches. Thus, 4-foot-long panels could be cross-grain knife-planed. When cutting cross-grain, a cleavage failure does not advance along the grain ahead of the knife edge. Hence, chipped grain or tear out, even along glue lines, is minimal. The surface from cross-grain knife planing is generally as good as or better than a surface abrasive-planed with a 36-grit belt. In a trial at Carbondale a spray lacquer finish was satisfactorily applied to cross-grain knife-planed walnut panels without sanding. However, in practice a small amount of sanding would probably be required for an acceptable finish.

[4]*P. Y. S. Chen and G. A. Cooper. The effect of prefreezing on the permeability of black walnut to water. Unpublished manuscript on file at North Cent. For. Exp. Stn., Carbondale, Ill. 1973.*

Cross-grain knife planing of dimension stock can be done with segmented helical cutterheads.[5] The cuttings must be butted against each other and aligned so their long axes are parallel to a tangent of the helix cutters. The minimum distance (D) from the leading corner to the trailing corner of each cutting must be equal to or greater than the shortest stock that can be butted end-to-end when knife planing conventionally along the grain. Black walnut cuttings 1 by 10 inches (D = 4.39 inches) have been satisfactorily cross-grain knife-planed with a segmented helical cutterhead. The shortest stock that could be fed through butted was 4 inches. The cuttings were oriented side-by-side parallel to a tangent of the helix angle and followed by a longer cutting parallel to the feed to push the shorter cuttings under the cutterhead.

Other research showed that a high-quality particleboard can be manufactured from cross-grain knife-planed flakes (Stewart and Lehmann 1973). Low-density particleboard manufactured from such flakes meets or exceeds the minimum property requirements of medium- and high-density particleboard. Virtually all of the cross-grain knife-planed shavings, including black walnut, can be made into high-quality particleboards, thus reducing waste from the machining operation and stretching the raw material supply. A trial black walnut particeboard was produced from cross-grained black walnut flakes in cooperation with the Forest Products Laboratory at Madison, Wisconsin, to show that black walnut cross-grain knife-planed flakes can be used in particleboards.

CONCLUSION

Recent survey information shows that significant additional sources of black walnut are short logs and trees on noncommercial forest land not reported in previous surveys. Also, to more completely utilize the total black walnut resource, improved processing methods have been developed. Production of walnut furniture dimension from low-quality material shows that an average of 75 percent of the International ¼-Inch Rule scaled volume can be recovered in the form of high-quality dimension. A promising drying method for dimension parts made from low-quality timber is prefreezing the pieces before kiln-drying to significantly reduce drying time and rejects. After drying the material can be machined, using either abrasive planing or knife- cross-grain planing to reduce the chipped grain, thereby reducing waste in surface machining.

---

[5]*H. A. Stewart. Segmented helical cutters provide good residue for particleboard and reduce machining noise. Manuscript in preparation for publication.*

GLOSSARY

Commercial forest land. — Forest land that is producing or is capable of producing crops of industrial wood and that is not withdrawn from timber utilization by statute or administrative regulation. Industrial wood includes commercial products such as saw logs and pulpwood, but excludes fuelwood and fence posts.

Growing-stock volume. — Net volume in cubic feet of sound wood in the boles of live sawtimber and poletimber trees from stump to a minimum 4.0-inch top diameter outside bark of the central stem or to the point where the central stem breaks into limbs.

Sawtimber volume. — Net volume in board feet (International ¼-Inch Rule) in the saw-log portions of live sawtimber trees from a 1-foot stump to a minimum 8.0-inch top diameter inside bark or to the point on the bole of sawtimber trees above which a saw log cannot be produced. A saw log is a log that is at least 8 feet long and meets the other standards of diameter and defect as specified for grade F1, F2, or F3 logs or for tie-and-timber class logs.

Short-log trees (Special Kentucky Survey). — Live trees 5.0 inches d.b.h. and larger that contain now or prospectively a usable 6- or 7-foot bolt. *(Indiana and Kansas Survey).* — Trees that contain one or more 8- to 11-foot saw logs and would qualify as growing stock except for the 12-foot log requirement. Although these trees are merchantable, the net volume is shown separately from growing stock.

Nonforest land. — Land that has never supported forests and lands formerly forested that are now developed for other uses. Includes areas used for crops, improved pasture, residential areas, city parks, and improved roads or power-line clearings of any width. If intermingled in forest areas, unimproved roads, trails, and nonforest strips must be more than 120 feet wide and clearings more than 1 acre in size to qualify as nonforest.

LITERATURE CITED

Blyth, James E. 1968. Veneer log production and consumption, North Central Region, 1966. USDA For. Serv. Resour. Bull. NC-5, 6 p., illus. North Cent. For. Exp. Stn., St. Paul, Minn.

Blyth, James E., Edwin Kallio, and John C. Callahan. 1969. Standing timber coefficients for Indiana walnut log production. USDA For. Serv. Res. Pap. NC-33, 9 p., illus. North Cent. For. Exp. Stn., St. Paul, Minn.

Chase, Clarence D., and John K. Strickler. 1968. Kansas woodlands. USDA For. Serv. Resour. Bull. NC-4, 50 p., illus. North Cent. For. Exp. Stn., St. Paul, Minn.

Cooper, G. A. 1972. Prefreezing reduces shrinkage and alters sorption in black walnut. For. Prod. J. 22(5): 54-60, illus.

Cooper, G. A., R. W. Erickson, and J. G. Haygreen. 1970. Drying behavior of prefrozen black walnut. For. Prod. J. 20(1): 30-35, illus.

Dunmire, D. E., E. F. Landt, and R. E. Bodkin. 1972. Logging residue is a source of valuable black walnut dimension. For. Prod. J. 22(1): 13-17, illus.

Ginnaty, Thomas P., Jr. 1970. Veneer-log production and receipts, North Central Region, 1968. USDA For. Serv. Resour. Bull. NC-10, 8 p., illus. North Cent. For. Exp. Stn., St. Paul, Minn.

Ginnaty, Thomas P., Jr. 1972. Veneer-log production and receipts, North Central Region, 1970. USDA For. Serv. Resour. Bull. NC-14, 8 p., illus. North Cent. For. Exp. Stn., St. Paul, Minn.

Illinois Cooperative Crop Reporting Service. 1972. Illinois timber prices. 2 p.

Lindmark, Ronald D., and Paul S. DeBald. 1969. Black walnut on nonforest land in Kentucky. USDA For. Serv. Resour. Bull. NE-16, 18 p., illus. Northeast. For. Exp. Stn., Upper Darby, Penn.

Quigley, Kenneth L., and Ronald D. Lindmark. 1967. A look at black walnut timber resources and industries. USDA For. Serv. Resour. Bull. NE-4, 28 p., illus. Northeast. For. Exp. Stn., Upper Darby, Penn.

Shumann, D. R. 1971. Dimension yields from black walnut lumber. USDA For. Serv. Res. Pap. FPL-162, 17 p., illus. For. Prod. Lab., Madison, Wis.

Spencer, John S., Jr. 1969. Indiana's timber. USDA For. Serv Resour. Bull. NC-7, 61 p., illus. North Cent. For. Exp. Stn., St. Paul, Minn.

Stewart, H. A. 1970a. Abrasive vs. knife planing. For. Prod. J. 20(7): 43-47, illus.

Stewart, H. A. 1970b. Cross-grain knife planing hard maple produces high-quality surfaces and flakes. For. Prod. J. 20(10): 39-42, illus.

Stewart, H. A. 1971. Cross-grain knife planing improves surface quality and utilization of aspen. USDA For. Serv. Res. Note NC-127, 4 p., illus. North Cent. For. Exp. Stn., St. Paul, Minn.

Stewart, Harold A., and William F. Lehmann. 1973. High-quality particleboard from cross-grain knife-planed hardwood flakes. For. Prod. J. (In press.)

USDA Forest Service. 1965. Timber trends in the United States. USDA For. Serv., For. Resour. Rep. 17, 235 p., illus.

USDA Forest Service. 1971. Unclaimed profits in black walnut. North Cent. For. Exp. Stn., St. Paul, Minn. 4 p., illus.

USDA Forest Service. 1972. Forest statistics for the United States, by State and region, 1970. 96 p., illus.

EVALUATION OF SELECTED WOOD PROPERTIES IN RELATION TO SOIL-SITE CONDITIONS

H. E. Wahlgren, *In Charge*
Timber Quality & Product Potential
Timber Utilization Research
Forest Products Laboratory
Madison, Wisconsin

ABSTRACT.—Relationships in black walnut wood color, specific gravity, extractive content, anatomical characteristics, machining, and mechanical properties were explored. The influence of geographic location, site quality, and growth conditions on these properties was also examined. Luminance was related to extractive content and to the combination of extractive content and some measure of wood density. Indiana trees differed significantly from Missouri trees by having: higher luminance value, lower extractive content, greater shrinkage, higher proportion of fibrous tissue with thinner cell walls, and smaller vessel lumens. No difference was detected in the physical characteristics or properties between trees from the two States.

It was 7 years ago that the first walnut workshop was held here in Carbondale, Illinois. The concern expressed then, I suspect, is the same now — what can be done to bring the supply of black walnut (*Juglans nigra* L.) lumber more in line with demand.

Specifically, the challenge issued by the keynote speaker, Ed Cliff, at that workshop still prevails as the charter of research efforts for all of us (USDA Forest Service 1966). Mr. Cliff alluded to three items of concern to meet the prospective needs for supplies of black walnut wood:

1. Stimulate diameter growth of growing stock trees.

2. Plant and grow superior type trees for timber.

3. Improve the wood quality of the growing trees.

It was the third point that motivated us in Wood Quality Research at the Forest Products Laboratory (FPL) to embark on a wood quality evaluation program for black walnut.

While forest managers the world over have accumulated considerable quantitative information on wood, it was not until the last decade that the need for qualitative information became evident.

The qualitative aspect, more appropriately referred to as timber quality, is by definition considered to be that combination of physical and chemical characteristics of a tree or its parts that permit the best utilization of the wood for its intended use. While such a definition may not be completely acceptable for all uses of wood, it does provide the framework for evaluating the quality of wood, based on its physical, mechanical, anatomical, and chemical characteristics.

Because no single unit expresses the quality of clear, straight-grained wood directly for all uses, wood quality is often described indirectly. That is, one or more properties of wood indicative of its suitability for a particular use is measured or assessed.

For the coniferous species, specific gravity or wood density has been the single index most evaluated by those concerned with an assessment of wood quality.

We have not been so fortunate when it comes to the hardwood species. The many and diversified uses, from pulpwood to furniture and paneling, have precluded development of a single unit to express the quality of wood. As a result, a number of factors or characteristics have been considered in our wood quality evaluations of black walnut.

At the previous workshop, it came to our attention that buyers of black walnut expressed a definite preference for logs from certain areas over others. The reasons for such preference are not definitely known. Some claim that defects such as bird peck, shake, and poor tree form are the main reasons for discrimination. Such defects may be more prevalent on trees growing near the borders of the species range or on poor sites. On the other hand, some think that discrimination by buyers of walnut logs from certain localities is from habit and without valid reason.

To shed some light on such preferences, we at the FPL embarked on a comprehensive research program on the quality of black walnut wood. The objectives of our studies were to determine whether differences exist in color and extractives, anatomical features, mechanical properties, and machining characteristics of wood from two different areas in Indiana and Missouri; from fast- and slow-grown trees; and from good and poor sites.

SAMPLING PROCEDURE

Thirty-two trees were selected from Indiana and Missouri, distributed equally within these States by site quality and by growth rate in a 2 by 2 by 2 factorial design (table 1).

Between 8 and 13 feet above ground, a 5-foot-long bolt was cut from each tree, and the age of the tree (bolt) and diameter-growth rate determined on both ends of each bolt. Diameter inside bark, heartwood diameter, and sapwood width were also determined for two site and growth subclasses (table 2).

A sample of the surface soil (15 cm.) was taken from around each sample tree; each was the composite of eight borings taken systematically within a 6-meter radius of the tree. A pit was also excavated, and the soil profiles described and classified at each location, including depth to mottling or impervious layer. The 5-foot bolts were sawn into 1¼ by 4¼-inch boards and from each bolt eight boards were randomly selected for the study. Following a light surface planing, each board was cut into four 1-foot-long pieces and one 6-inch randomly selected section. The 6-inch section provided the samples for determining color, wood structure, shrinkage, and extractive content. The 12-inch-long pieces were dried to 12 percent moisture content and provided the samples for the machining and strength tests.

RELATIONSHIP OF WOOD COLOR TO SOIL PROPERTIES AND SITE

There has been very little information on the effects of specific environmental factors on heartwood color. There are two different views on the origins or movements of extractives to form heartwood. In one view it is believed that extractives are produced in the cambium or outer sapwood and translocated by the rays to the heartwood (Stewart 1966). In contrast, the other view is that extractives are formed *in situ* in sapwood cells that become heartwood cells (Hillis 1962, 1968). In either case, therefore, it was suspect that soil properties important for black walnut growth could affect wood color through their effects on the metabolism of the tree.

One of the first attempts at assessing the color characteristics of heartwood in trees from different geographic areas was by Sullivan (1967). He found significant within-species differences in the color properties of yellow-poplar and black cherry that were related to the geographic location of the trees. Moslemi (1967) at Southern Illinois University further demonstrated that differences in walnut wood color could be determined

Table 1. — *Sampling design for black walnut trees*

Site class	Growth class	Missouri			Indiana		
		Trees	Average growth rate	50-yr. site index	Trees	Average growth rate	50-yr. site index
		No.	Rings/cm.	Ft.	No.	Rings/cm.	Ft.
Good	Fast	4	3.3	60	4	2.8	80
	Slow	4	4.2	58	4	3.9	78
Poor	Fast	4	3.6	55	4	2.8	76
	Slow	4	4.2	57	4	4.1	67

18

Table 2. — *Values of bolt characteristics for black walnut trees from Indiana and Missouri*[1]

INDIANA

Site class	Growth class	Diameter inside bark	Heartwood diameter	Sapwood width	Age	Growth rate
		In.	In.	In.	Yrs.	Rings/in.
Good	Fast	13.0	10.6	2.4	45	7.2
	Slow	10.9	9.4	1.5	70	12.9
Poor	Fast	15.2	12.2	2.6	52	7.2
	Slow	12.0	10.4	1.6	63	10.5
MISSOURI						
Good	Fast	13.7	12.0	1.7	55	8.3
	Slow	11.6	9.8	1.8	62	10.6
Poor	Fast	12.7	11.1	1.6	57	9.1
	Slow	11.0	9.5	1.5	58	10.6

1/ The values are the average of four trees and represent the 8- to 13-foot aboveground portion of the tree.

by spectrophotometric analysis. Our work on black walnut began when Nelson *et al.* (1969) evaluated the color of heartwood samples, according to the International Commission on Illumination (I.C.I.) system. Spectrophotometric analyses were used to determine the following properties: (1) percent luminance — the brightness or lightness of the color, (2) dominant wavelength — related directly to the hue of the color, and (3) percent purity — percentage of principal hue in the color.

Results of this portion of the study conducted by Nelson indicated that greater differences between trees were found in luminance than in dominant wavelength and purity. Mean tree luminance was significantly higher for the Indiana-grown trees than for the Missouri-grown. The difference is pertinent because it may indicate a trend toward easily distinguishable luminance difference in walnut from more widely separated geographic areas.

Although the results did not reflect a significant difference between wood from sites of different quality, there were indications that on the poor sites the wood was lower in luminance and higher in dominant wavelength.

The relationships of the three color parameters with soil properties were evaluated by Nelson *et al.* (1969) and Maeglin and Nelson (1970) by regression analysis.

The analysis revealed variations in soil fertility were correlated with differences in wood color between individual sample trees. While the range of observed site quality was rather limited, the poorer sites showed a tendency toward darker, more red heartwood (lower luminance, higher dominant wavelength). In terms of simple linear regression analyses, pH consistently had the highest correlation with each of the three color values. In the two variable combinations this did not hold true, for in no case was pH included in the combination with the highest R^2. The relationship of pH in the simple regressions is believed to be related to the effect of pH on other soil properties that may directly affect wood color.

On the whole, mean tree luminance was most highly related to available P, exchangeable Ca, exchangeable Mg, and depth to mottling or impervious layer. These findings allow for the possibility of one day controlling wood color by manipulating the soil by fertilization or by other soil management techniques.

RELATIONSHIP OF WOOD COLOR TO ANATOMICAL CHARACTERISTICS

Based on the same specimens used by Nelson in the color evaluation, Hiller *et al.* (1972) determined whether the differences in color observed by Nelson could be related to specific gravity, structure, or extractive content of the wood. A second objective was to determine whether growth rate and site class affected the physical and anatomical characteristics of black walnut. While very little appears in the literature on these effects (Dillow and Hawker 1971, Boyce *et al.* 1970), the inverse relationship of shrinkage to extractive content is well known (Cooper 1971, 1972).

The structural features examined by Hiller *et al.* included:

> Percentage of area occupied by vessel lumens.
> Percentage of area occupied by normal fibers.
> Percentage of area occupied by gelatinous fibers.
> Average number of vessels per mm.^{2}.
> Average vessel lumen area (mm.^{2}).
> Cross-sectional dimensions of the fibers.
> Percent extractives.
> Specific gravity of fibrous tissue.

The amount of extractives based on the specific gravity specimens (end matched to color and wood structure) was determined by the TAPPI standard method (1959) and expressed as a percentage of the extractive-free weight of the wood. Specific gravity was determined from the extractive-free ovendry weight and the volume of the specimens in the water-saturated condition.

Single and multiple linear regression analyses were used to determine the relationships between the wood color parameters and the structural features mentioned previously.

Results of analyses based on values for individual test specimens and on average values for bolts were essentially the same. Dominant wavelength and percent purity were not significantly related to any single variable (structural features) or to any combination of variables. The third dependent variable, percent luminance, was, however, significantly related to percent extractives and to the specific gravity of the fibrous tissue, or other measures of wood density.

The results further indicated that wood from Indiana had lower percent extractives than that from Missouri. In addition, the following differences in wood characteristics between the States were found:

Trees from Indiana had thinner cell walls.

Trees from Indiana had a lower percent cross-sectional area occupied by vessel lumens.

Trees from Indiana had smaller average vessel lumen areas.

Wood from the two States did not differ in gelatinous fiber content nor did the regression analyses show any relationship between that characteristic and the color of the wood. In this regard it is interesting that when States are ignored, the wood from good sites had significantly more gelatinous fibers than the wood from poor sites. Similarly, wood from the slow-growing trees had a significantly higher percent of gelatinous fibers than did the fast-growing trees.

Nelson *et al.* (1969) found a relationship between wood color and some soil properties; it is interesting to speculate that soil properties might also affect the extractive content of wood. Because extractive content is negatively related to the shrinkage of wood, it may be the factor of greater importance for the industry. It may also be possible in the future to control not only the color but also the shrinkage characteristics of wood by controlling forest management practices.

MECHANICAL, PHYSICAL, AND MACHINING PROPERTIES

This portion of the study, conducted by Schumann (1973) was also based on wood specimens from the sample of Nelson *et al.* (1969). The objective was to determine whether the anatomical characteristics measured by Hiller *et al.* (1972) were related to the machining and mechanical properties of wood. The machining tests conducted by Schumann were associated with planing, shaping, and turning; and the mechanical properties evaluated were hardness and toughness. Three physical characteristics — shrinkage, slope of grain, and specific gravity — were also examined.

Volumetric shrinkage, based on dimensions of the sample when green and when dried to 12 percent moisture content, was greater in the Indiana-grown black walnut (table 3).

Extractive content and volumetric shrinkage were significantly and negatively correlated. That is to say, the Indiana material, with its higher luminance value and lower extractive content, exhibited greater shrinkage than the Missouri samples.

Table 3. — *Means and differences of mechanical and physical properties of black walnut by State of origin, site class, and growth rate. Each value is the average of 16 trees*

Classification	Extractive content	Volumetric shrinkage[1]	Specific gravity[2]	Hardness	Toughness	Slope of grain
	Percent	Percent		Pounds	In.-Pounds	Percent
State:						
Indiana	5.3	5.14	0.556	1,154	251.9	6.7
Missouri	6.6	4.75	.560	1,131	239.9	4.3
Difference	[3]1.3	[4].39	.004	23	12.0	[4]2.4
Site quality:						
Good	5.5	5.05	.563	1,172	272.7	5.1
Poor	6.5	4.84	.554	1,113	219.0	5.9
Difference	1.0	.21	.009	59	[4]53.7	.8
Growth rate:						
Fast	6.2	5.00	.565	1,170	247.7	5.4
Slow	5.7	4.90	.551	1,115	244.0	5.6
Difference	.5	.10	.014	55	3.7	.2

[1] Based on dimension when green and then dried to 12 percent moisture content.
[2] Based on volume at 12 percent moisture content and ovendry weight.
[3] Difference significant at 0.05 level.
[4] Difference significant at 0.01 level.

The slope of grain was greater in the Indiana specimens, but the amount did not appreciably affect any of the machining or mechanical properties. In both Indiana and Missouri, the good sites produced tougher wood, which was correlated with specific gravity and extractive content. An increase in specific gravity and extractive content will, therefore, correspondingly reflect an increase in toughness.

Shaping and turning tests indicated that geographic location, site quality, and growth rate did not affect the quality of the specimens. Similarly, none of the anatomical or physical characteristics affected the quality of the resultant shaping and turning specimens. All specimens machined well.

Specific gravity proved to be the one most important characteristic in evaluating machining and mechanical properties of black walnut. As pointed out by Schumann (1973), it accounted for 45 percent of the variation observed in the hardness values, 8 percent of the variation in toughness values, and 9 percent of the variation in planing. Specific gravity was also correlated with volumetric shrinkage and slope of grain.

SUMMARY

The reasons that black walnut wood from one area is preferred to that from another area were partially explained by the intrinsic characteristics measured in this detailed study.

Of the three color parameters measured, larger differences were found in heartwood luminance than in dominant wavelength or purity. Indiana-grown walnut heartwood had higher luminance than Missouri-grown. Luminance was significantly related to extractive content and specific gravity. Extractive content and volumetric shrinkage were significantly and negatively correlated. The Indiana material had higher luminance, less extractives, exhibited greater volumetric shrinkage, had thinner cell walls, and smaller vessel lumens than the Missouri-grown walnut.

Regression analyses indicated that variations in soil fertility were correlated with differences in wood color between individual sample trees. Available P, exchangeable K, Ca, Mg, total N, and pH were found to be most important in relation to color variation.

21

While no differences were found in mechanical properties between trees from the two States, a significant difference was found between sites. Specimens from the good sites had substantially higher toughness values than those from the poor sites. No difference in hardness was detectable among States, sites, or growth conditions.

Specific gravity was the important characteristic in evaluating the machining and mechanical properties of black walnut. It accounted for 45 percent of the observed variations in hardness values, 8 percent in toughness values, and 9 percent of the variation in planing.

The results suggest the possibility of controlling the desirable characteristics by manipulating forest management practices and by improving the quality of black walnut through genetic means.

LITERATURE CITED

Boyce, S. G., M. Kaeiser, and C. F. Bey. 1970. Variation of some wood features in five black walnut trees. For. Sci. 16(1): 95-100.

Cooper, Glenn A. 1971. Black walnut extractives availability is influenced by thawing-to-extraction time. For. Prod. J. 21(10): 44, 45.

Cooper, Glenn A. 1972. Prefreezing reduces shrinkage and alters sorption in black walnut. For. Prod. J. 22(5): 54-60.

Dillow, Martha K., and Norman L. Hawker. 1971. Annotated bibliography of walnut — supplement No. 1. USDA For. Serv. Res. Pap. NC-70, 23 p. North Cent. For. Exp. Stn., St. Paul, Minn.

Hiller, Charlotte, F. Freese, and Diana Smith. 1972. Relationships in black walnut heartwood between color and other physical and anatomical characteristics. Wood & Fiber 4(1): 38-42.

Hillis, W. E. 1962. The distribution and formation of polyphenols within the tree. In Wood extractives and their significance to the pulp and paper industry. p. 59-131. New York: Academic Press, Inc.

Hillis, W. E. 1968. Chemical aspects of heartwood formation. Wood Sci. Technol. 2: 241-259.

Maeglin, R., and N. Nelson. 1970. Surface soil properties of black walnut sites in relationship to wood color. Soil Sci. Soc. Am. Proc. 34(1): 142-146.

Moslemi, Ali A. 1967. Quantitative color measurement for black walnut wood. USDA For. Serv. Res. Pap. NC-17, 16 p. North Cent. For. Exp. Stn., St. Paul, Minn.

Nelson, N., R. Maeglin, and H. Wahlgren. 1969. Relationship of black walnut wood color to soil properties and site. Wood & Fiber 1(1): 29-37.

Schumann, David R. 1973. Mechanical, physical, and machining properties of black walnut from Indiana and Missouri. Wood & Fiber. (In press.)

Stewart, C. M. 1966. Excretion and heartwood formation in living trees. Science 153: 1068-1074.

Sullivan, J. D. 1967. Color characterization of wood: color parameters of individual species. For. Prod. J. 17: 25-29.

Technical Association of the Pulp and Paper Industry (TAPPI). 1959. Standard T 12 M-59, preparation of extractive-free wood.

USDA Forest Service. 1966. Black walnut culture. North Cent. For. Exp. Stn., St. Paul, Minn. 94 p.

FEDERAL TRADE COMMISSION GUIDES AND THEIR EFFECTS ON THE CONSUMER

Donald H. Gott, *Executive Director*
Fine Hardwoods – American Walnut Association
Chicago, Illinois

ABSTRACT.—Walnut and fine hardwoods consumer products now protected by Federal Trade Commission Guides are described. The Guides are interpreted, and the enforcement policies are explained; the consumer products still urgently in need of similar regulations are mentioned. Association activities in furniture case goods surveys and tag and label promotions are also described.

The phrase, "consumer protection," is a much used and much needed part of today's scene. From the Federal government on down, divisions, agencies, and bureaus have been established in order to provide the consumer with a fair deal on his purchased commodities or services. As is usually the case with something new, a variety of things have been overemphasized; but perhaps more important, some consumer goods which have been underemphasized are finally being recognized as demanding immediate corrective action.

Actually, to pinpoint this need, "consumerism" (for want of a better word) has replaced ecology as a major issue for 1973. This is borne out by a recent poll of public relations directors of large corporations which disclosed that nearly 50 percent of the commercial, industrial, and consumer respondents are planning major government relations programs as part of their 1973 budget, a decided increase over 1972.

One of the agencies now recognizing these needs is the Federal Trade Commission, Washington, D.C. Among its many fields of activity was the Decorative Wall Paneling Industry and its own particular need for "guidance concerning legal requirements applicable to this industry in the interest of protecting the public and effecting more widespread and equitable observance of the laws administered by the Commission."

Hence, after a full public hearing held on March 12, 1970, the Commission adopted Guides for the Decorative Wall Paneling Industry on December 15, 1971, which were to become effective 1 year later. This provided 1 entire year for members of the industry to acquaint themselves "with a sufficient number of examples to afford them meaningful guidance in the conduct of their affairs so as to avoid legal difficulties."

The intentions of these guides and others to follow — namely, Guides for the Household Furniture Industry — are to ensure against the prospective purchaser being misled by the appearance of a product, or by descriptions, designations, advertising, labeling, or other promotional means, into thinking the product is different from that which is actually offered. In summary, all guides may be brought under the Federal Trade Commission Act, which makes it illegal for one to engage in unfair methods of competition and unfair or deceptive acts or practices in commerce. Copies of guides and interpretations can be had on request from the Division of Rules and Guides, Bureau of Consumer Protection, Federal Trade Commission, Washington, D.C. 20580.

Examples of representations considered false in the Guides for Decorative Wall Paneling are:

1.—Describing a particleboard, flakeboard, hardboard, fiberboard, chipcore or plywood panel as "solid wood."

2.—Describing as "natural wood grain" a simulated grain design which has been printed on, attached to, or simulated in any other manner on the surface of an industry product.

3.—Describing a nonlumber product, such as particleboard, hardboard, fiberboard, flakeboard, and products of similar composition, as "wood." Although such products are composed of wood particles or wood fibers, they should not be represented without qualification as "wood" but may be described as "particleboard," "hardboard," "fiberboard," "wood product," or by any applicable nondeceptive word or term.

4.—Describing as "walnut," "in walnut," "genuine walnut," "walnut panel," or "walnut plywood" a panel having only a face veneer of walnut. Proper descriptions would include "walnut veneer face", "walnut veneer surface," "walnut veneer," or "walnut veneered plywood."

5.—Describing as "walnut veneer" a panel having a face veneer not entirely of walnut. If a wood name is used to describe a panel having more than one kind of wood in the face veneer then all of the woods in the face veneers should be named or otherwise identified (e.g., "walnut and cherry veneers" or "walnut and other hardwood veneers").

6.—Using unqualified phrases such as "woodpattern" or "woodgrain finish" to describe a panel having a wood surface which has been stamped, rolled, pressed, or otherwise processed in such manner as to change the natural wood grain design. Proper descriptions would include "simulated woodgrain finish," "imitation grain figure," or "simulated walnut grain finish on birch face veneer."

7.—Has an exposed surface of plastic, metal, vinyl, hardboard, particleboard, or other material not possessing a natural wood grain structure but which has an appearance simulating that of a wood grain. Depending on the composition, proper descriptions would include "simulated walnut finish on plastic face," "vinyl surface with simulated pecan finish," "simulated birch finish on hardboard," "mahogany grained plastic," or other nondeceptive phrases.

8.—Has a wood surface finished by means of staining, decalcomania, printing, paper coating, or other process so as to have the appearance of a different kind of wood. Depending on the composition, proper descriptions would include "mahogany finished gum plywood," "walnut stained plywood," "walnut finish on pecan veneer face," or "cherry grain design on hardwood plywood."

Also, under the "Deceptive Use of Wood Names" section, please note the following: "The unqualified term 'walnut' should not be used to describe wood other than genuine solid walnut (genus *Juglans*). The

term 'black walnut' should be applied only to the species *Juglans nigra*."

Under the section entitled "Imitations of Materials Other Than Wood," this should be noted: "A hardboard panel having an imitation marble finish should not be described without qualification as 'marble,' 'onyx,' 'travertine,' or 'travertine marble finish.' Proper descriptions would include 'simulated marble finish,' 'imitation marble-textured,' 'marble pattern on plastic faced hardboard,' 'simulated travertine or hardboard,' 'marble pattern on vinyl-faced hardboard,' or other nondeceptive terms."

And finally, paneling industry members should not: "(a) remove, obliterate, deface, change, alter, conceal, or make illegible any information these Guides provide be disclosed on industry products, without replacing the same before sale, resale, or distribution for sale with a proper mark or label meeting the provisions of these Guides; or (b) sell, resell, or distribute any industry product without its being marked or labeled and described in accordance with the provisions of these Guides."

All of the above violations if ignored and continued, place the violator subject to severe daily fines, imprisonment, or both. In addition to their Washington headquarters, the Federal Trade Commission has district offices in most major cities. Their personnel, after December 15, 1972, are prepared to enforce the law wherever established violations have been reported. These are the effective ways and means FTC Guides will be and are being endorsed.

Now that Mr. and Mrs. Consumer know what they are purchasing in wall panels, what other consumer goods desperately need similar effective insurance against wood imitations? Obviously, household furniture, cabinets, and home entertainment items come to mind. To this end, the Federal Trade Commission has before its Board of Commissioners similar guides pertaining to household furniture that contain similar language and similar case violations to those listed in the guides for wall paneling. Many manufacturers define their wood imitations properly, but after bedroom and dining room suites reach the retail floor, these identifications seem to mysteriously disappear.

For the last 39 years, our Association has tallied every bedroom and dining room suite shown at the two most important international furniture markets — usually April and October (tables 1 and 2). This survey

Table. 1—*Southern Furniture market survey, bedroom and dining room suites, October 1971 and 1972.*

BY WOODS

Wood or style	Number of suites 1971	Number of suites 1972	Percentage of total 1971	Percentage of total 1972	Percentage change
Walnut S & V[1]	253	202	9.5	7.7	-1.8
Mahogany S & V	73	50	2.7	1.9	- .6
Cherry S & V	210	113	7.9	4.3	-3.6
Maple S & V	273	231	10.2	8.9	-1.3
Oak S & V	297	349	11.1	13.4	+2.3
Butternut S & V	3	34	.1	1.3	+1.2
Pecan S & V	380	347	14.2	13.3	- .9
Birch S & V	50	42	1.9	1.6	- .3
Pine S & V	158	172	5.9	6.6	+ .7
Prints & plastics	609	717	22.8	27.4	+4.6
Painted	260	271	9.7	10.4	+ .7
Other solids[2]	28	20	1.0	.8	- .2
Other veneers[2]	79	62	3.0	2.4	- .6
Total	2,673	2,610	100	100	

BY STYLES

	1971	1972	1971	1972	change
Modern	--	--	17.4	18.5	+1.1
Commercial modern	--	--	.6	2.0	+1.4
Total modern	--	--	18.0	20.5	+2.5
Provincial	--	--	7.6	5.8	-1.8
Court	--	--	3.3	1.0	-2.3
Total French	--	--	10.9	6.8	-4.1
Early American Colonial Federal	--	--	26.8	27.4	+ .6
Italian	--	--	13.8	5.8	-8.0
Spanish	--	--	26.6	34.2	+7.6
English	--	--	3.8	5.3	+1.5
Miscellaneous	--	--	.1	--	- .1

[1] S = solids; V = veneers.
[2] Includes: elm, prima vera, rosewood, teak, avedire, acacia, ash, sycamore, paldao, gum andiroba, bamboo, olive burl, poplar, persimmon, ebanwood, mozambique, cordia, wenge, and others not listed separately.

is all-embracing, as it covers every showroom in the market area. It provides three elements: wood species, style, and finish. If you will note the percentage of "Prints and Plastics" as higher than "Pecan and Oak" combined, you will then realize the necessity for truthful identification of these wood imitations. It gives real cause to wonder just how many consumers are positive they purchased the genuine, when they actually are the possessors of a paper print on a particle-board base. For the past 40 years the Association has also publicized and promoted its "hang-tag" program to assist the purchaser of genuine walnut products (fig. 1). Little good these tags do, which we sell to the manufacturer, if they are removed before the product is sold to the consumer.

Fortunately for all, the promulgating of the proposed Household Furniture Guides by the Federal Trade Commission will be the effective means to stop these deceptions. It is one of the prime objectives of the Fine Hardwoods-American Walnut Association to make every effort to see this accomplished. We feel everyone should describe any product truthfully, tell the public what it is, and identify its construction with a label or tag which legally cannot be removed. Then and only then will the consumer be afforded an honest choice of either the genuine or the imitation.

Table 2.—*Southern furniture market survey, bedroom and dining room suites by wood finish, October 1971 and 1972.*   (In percent)

WALNUT

Finish	Bedroom suites 1971	Bedroom suites 1972	Dining room suites 1971	Dining room suites 1972
	[1] (119)	[1] (99)	[1](134)	[1](103)
Dark	7.6	4.1	10.4	17.5
Walnut brown	56.3	43.4	56.7	36.9
Fruitwood brown	5.1	11.1	6.0	10.6
Light brown	16.0	11.1	11.2	7.8
Grey brown	2.5	1.0	--	--
Tan and honey	1.7	3.0	3.7	3.9
Red brown dark	10.9	26.3	11.2	23.3
Other natural wood tones	--	--	.8	--

OTHER WOODS

Finish	Bedroom suites 1971	Bedroom suites 1972	Dining room suites 1971	Dining room suites 1972
	[1](1,056)	[1](740)	[1](755)	[1](680)
Dark	19.9	17.8	15.9	18.5
Walnut brown	20.1	21.5	13.9	14.1
Fruitwood brown	17.1	25.1	19.3	16.0
Light brown	23.0	11.8	12.9	19.1
Grey brown	4.1	5.7	2.2	.8
Tan and honey	10.3	9.5	22.1	18.3
Red brown dark	4.6	6.9	11.2	10.9
Other natural wood tones	.9	1.7	2.5	2.3

PRINTS-PLASTICS

Finish	Bedroom suites 1971	Bedroom suites 1972	Dining room suites 1971	Dining room suites 1972
	[1] (379)	[1](462)	[1](230)	[1](255)
Dark	12.8	32.0	10.4	13.7
Walnut brown	26.6	24.0	12.6	19.6
Fruitwood brown	18.6	14.9	27.4	25.1
Light brown	22.9	13.6	15.2	22.8
Grey brown	7.9	3.0	8.7	--
Tan and honey	8.4	6.3	13.9	9.0
Red brown dark	1.0	1.5	11.3	3.9
Other natural wood tones	1.8	4.5	.5	5.9

[1] Numbers in parenthesis = number of suites.

— *You Have the Right to Know* —

SOLID WALNUT — American Walnut

ALL VENEERS AND SOLIDS OF GENUINE WALNUT — American Walnut

Trade names which contain the word "walnut" may be misleading. There may be less walnut in the piece than you suppose, says a leading designer. Read information tags, such as those above, with care, he continues, because you have the right to know.
Tags which read "Solid Walnut" indicate that all exposed parts are solid wood. Tags which read "Genuine Walnut" mean that exposed parts are walnut veneers and walnut solids. If the furniture is not tagged, insist on information about the materials used in the piece. Both tags shown assure you that the furniture contains no printed imitation grains.

Figure 1.—*Examples of tags used on walnut products to protect the consumer.*

25

FOREST PRODUCTS REGULATORY LEGISLATION

John A. Sester, *Staff Forester*
Forest Products, Division of Forestry
Department of Conservation
Springfield, Illinois

ABSTRACT.—The intent of the Illinois Timber Buyers Licensing Act is to protect the landowner's right to receive monies due for timber sold, and to protect against timber piracy. The law requires anyone buying timber from the timber owner to be licensed. To obtain a license a surety bond must be posted. Amount of bonding surety is based on total timber purchases. Anyone transporting two or more logs or Christmas trees on any road in Illinois may be required to show proof of ownership under provisions of the Forest Products Transportation Act.

The Licensing Act has been on the books for a period of 5 years. From its original form it has undergone considerable change. The biggest change was 2 years after its original passage.

The original Act was written by the Illinois Agricultural Association, which does not have a forester. It did not license the small timber buyer but rather required the licensing of only timber buyers with three or more employees. Thus, over half of the timber buyers in Illinois were not required to post a bond and be licensed. Most of the problems regarding nonpayment for timber purchased developed within the ranks of these "smaller" buyers.

That law was not only ineffectual but, in the opinion of our Department lawyer, unconstitutional. The Division of Forestry took it upon itself to completely rewrite the statute in its present general form. We did request (and our recommendations were passed) some amendments to the law this year. Most of these amendments were points of clarification. The most potent amendment provided that lands adjacent to the purchase area were covered by the bond of the licensee. Without this amendment, buyers or loggers cutting over the line were not jeopardizing their bond or license.

The average timber owner sells timber only once or twice during his lifetime. Consequently, he is not familiar with the market or the pitfalls that can beset him. The intent of this statute is to protect the landowner's right to receive monies due for timber sold, and to protect him against timber piracy.

Simply stated, the law requires that anyone buying timber in Illinois after January 1, 1970, (from the owner or his representative) be licensed by the Department of Conservation. This is true of buyers living in the State as well as out-of-State buyers. Timber does not include firewood, Christmas trees, fruit or ornamental trees. The person who occasionally purchases timber for his own use and not for resale does not need a license. For instance, a farmer who buys some trees or logs to have sawed into drags, fencing, siding, etc., for use on his farm would be an occasional purchaser.

Cooperation and support of the primary wood-using industry has been excellent. Objections have been minimal — fewer than we anticipated. When an objection is aired, the intent of the law is explained to the buyer. After this he generally becomes a staunch supporter not only of the law but of our forestry programs.

This "getting with the program" has been a very definite side benefit of the law. It has drawn buyers, cutters, and others into our offices, thus expanding our contacts with these people, usually to their benefit.

To obtain this annual license a buyer must:

1. Make application.

2. Pay certificate and filing fees of $30.

3. Supply bonding surety in the amount of 10 percent of his total timber purchases for the preceding year (minimum $400, maximum $10,000).

The bonding requirement is the real "meat" of the license. Bond can be supplied by either:

1. Surety bond (average cost $20 per $1,000).

2. Bank certificate of deposit (interest paid to timber buyer).

The buyer's bond is available to make restitution to timber owners who are not paid the agreed price for timber purchased. Here the key word is *agreed*. As long as the buyer pays the agreed price and cuts only the timber bought, the requirements of the Licensing Act are satisfied. We do not establish prices, or guarantee any other agreements of the sales contract under this law.

There are built-in protections for the timber buyer's rights also. We must give written notice of any violation or noncompliance. He has the right to request a hearing to present his side of the story. Only after these steps can we request the Attorney General to institute proceedings to have the buyer's bond forfeited.

Besides having his money (surety bond or certificate of deposit) on the line, there are some real teeth in the law. Conviction of violating any of the Act's provisions can mean a fine of not less than $100 (up to $1,000), or imprisonment of not more than 6 months, or both.

To date we have had 65 arrests. Enforcement and actual arrests are handled by the Department of Conservation's Division of Law Enforcement. Our field personnel cooperate with these law officers by supplying any technical assistance needed, information on buyers, and leads on violators.

We think we now have a fair and equitable law that can be used to ferret out the unscrupulous element of the timber industry. Once this is done, public confidence will be restored in the timber industry.

FOREST PRODUCTS TRANSPORTATION ACT

The Forest Products Transportation Act was passed by the last legislative session on our recommendations. Principally it was aimed at walnut pilferage, although it will be a useful tool in all timber thievery cases. For instance, 2 weeks ago a complete 80-acre tract, absentee-owned, was completely cut over by a timber thief. Even if the cutter who stole this timber had been stopped, there would have been no law or regulation (ICC does not cover the transportation of rough wood products) requiring this man to prove ownership, or even divulge where he was getting the logs.

ILLINOIS TIMBER BUYERS LICENSING ACT

In Illinois the public had developed attitudes toward the timber industry that could no longer be ignored. We must admit that there was solid justification for the poor image the industry had. Complaints of timber buying malpractices were a common occurrence in our office.

The ways of "skinning" the timber owner were as numerous and varied as there were timber buyers, or so it seemed. Not uncommon were such malpractices as the "cut now — pay later" operator (he cuts the timber and is supposed to return with the owner's money when he is paid at the mill — often he does not return), and accidentally on-purpose over-the-line cutting. Then, of course, we don't want to forget the out-and-out stealing of timber.

The Timber Buyers Licensing Act was a tool put in our hands by the legislature to stop these practices. We have had a marked degree of success. Administration and enforcement of the law began on January 1, 1970. Since that time, 25 complaints have been lodged against the 400-plus yearly licensed buyers.

THE SIGNIFICANCE OF LOG AND TREE GRADING SYSTEMS

Robert Massengale, *Forest Products Specialist*
Missouri Department of Conservation
Jefferson City, Missouri

ABSTRACT.—Everyone who owns or plans on owning a walnut tree is interested in the value of that tree. Black walnut value may be measured by the nut production, the rate of tree growth, the shade it provides, or eventually the products it yields. Value is generally measured by tree or log grades, which for practical purposes are the same. Almost every manufacturing plant has its own grade rule that has been developed through experience.

The number, type, and location of defects are common to all grading systems. Defects generally fall into two categories: those that are natural or caused by some external force upon the tree, and those that are created by man in his manufacturing or processing of the tree. Understanding defects and their importance to the manufacturing of the final product will help the timber landowner better understand the value of his resource and will guide him toward using the proper forest management practices.

All of us present today have an interest in black walnut, in one way or another. If there is one item that we might agree upon, it probably is that we all want quality in the walnut product of our interest. Some of you are more interested in growing and managing walnut for scientific purposes. Others may be more interested in the tree's nut crop. And, of course, others are interested in the wood products the tree produces. We also share an interest in the economics of the tree and its products. I recently heard that a number of trees in California that had been excellent nut producers were placed on the market for their wood because they had ceased to provide the nut crop for which they had been planted. This wood, however, will find a ready market in the lumber and gunstock industries and will continue to be of benefit to man long after the intended use of the trees has ended. We know that the trees we plant and grow today should eventually provide wood products for our use. We want these products to be of the highest quality. It stands to reason, therefore, that anything we can do now to improve future quality is really a move in the right direction.

I've been asked to talk a little about tree and log grades. Essentially, there is no difference between standing tree and log grades. This is only true, however, if the cutter makes the cuts at the same places in the tree as the buyer had envisioned when he measured and scaled the tree. I recall a story related by forester Eldon Heflin of our Department concerning a landowner he had worked with. A buyer had mentioned to this man that his company bought veneer logs down to 6 and 7 feet long. While this is true, the longer logs are much preferred and bring more money. This landowner proceeded to cut up some 40 good trees into 6- and 7-foot lengths. A beautiful 12-foot veneer log was cut into two 6-foot lengths. This sale should have brought him about $3,000, but he ended up with slightly less than $500. Since the walnut cutters and the buyers work closely together, we feel it's very much to the landowner's advantage to let the buyer bring in his own cutter to get the best products possible from the trees. Actually, this is a manufacturing problem and the buyer will scale the tree for its highest value. The cutter must cut the tree to the same specifications to maintain the highest value.

The manufacturers of walnut products have developed different grading systems over the years. Unfortunately, there is no single system that satisfies everyone in the industry, because each manufacturer can use different materials depending on its product. The systems in use today vary considerably; some employ alphabetical grades, some use numerical ratings, and some use a combination of the two.

The terms "grade" and "value" in dealing with walnut are almost synonymous. Some companies in the walnut business apply a price rather than a grade to a tree. Others use a grade system of the type I've mentioned, and then relate this grade to a price. What this all boils down to is that the manufacturers know through experience just about what they can get out of a tree of a certain size. They also know that if the tree has defects, they will get less than the full volume of material. They figure the loss due to defects, their costs and profit, and arrive at a value for the tree or log. The company must make a profit to stay in business. I want to add, however, that they sometimes get fooled on quality and lose money on a particular sale or group of logs. It is necessary, therefore, that they make this up on other sales so that they average out in the black. You really don't know what's inside a log until you open it up, and by then it's too late to do anything about what it has cost you. By making a profit, of course, the industry is able to assure landowners that it will be there to buy their trees when they reach maturity.

Each type of walnut manufacturer is able to utilize a somewhat different type of walnut. The market for veneer today requires relatively straight-grained material in lengths 9 feet and longer. Sapwood in the veneer industry is generally considered a defect. The lumber and furniture industries use lumber grades from FAS down to #2 Common, and because lumber is almost always steamed to darken the sap, sapwood is not a defect. In gunstock manufacturing no steaming is allowed because it destroys the color contrasts. Only limited sapwood is allowed. Incidentally, the fancy gunstocks come from portions of the tree where lumber and veneer are not normally obtained, such as a crotch, burl, or the stump.

Because the industry uses tree and log grades to determine the amount of useful material they will get out of a particular tree or log, the number of defects is all-important. The common ground of all grading systems is the identification of defects and the location of these defects in the particular tree or log.

As I mentioned earlier, defects vary according to the needs of the manufacturer. We might define a defect simply as unusable material. I break defects into two general groups: (1) those that are in the log or tree, including natural and man-caused defects, and (2) those that man creates by mis-manufacturing.

Let's discuss the first group first because it is the largest. Natural defects include such things as unsound knots, sound knots, ring shake or separation, sapwood in some cases, deadwood, rot, tension wood, color variation, splits, and bird peck. Also included are defects caused by such things as fence wire, glass insulators, spikes, and gate hinges that man has decorated the tree with. Man also occasionally damages the tree with mechanical equipment or by fire, both of which later become defects or contribute to defects.

The second group, manufacturing defects, includes such things as cutting to incorrect lengths, splitting the tree, pulling fibers or splinters from the center of the log, allowing the log to lie in the woods too long where rot can start, and all of the associated defects from drying both in the log and in the products. These are generally splits and checks, warp, bow, crook, and honeycomb.

I have a number of slides with me to illustrate many of these defects, so if I have a little more time I'll go quickly through these slides and show you just what some of these defects are. I hope you will then relate these defects to trees you have and will be able to understand tree and log grading a little better as a result.

CULTURE: PAST, PRESENT, AND FUTURE

F. Bryan Clark, *Assistant Director*
North Central Forest Experiment Station

ABSTRACT.—Black walnut culture began in the U.S. and Europe soon after colonization. Even so, commercial production of black walnut timber is still restricted primarily to the U.S. and Canada, but interest abroad continues. Present cultural practices are based on many years of experience and recent intensified research. Continuing research and additional experience are needed to improve practices. Research efforts are especially lacking in protection from insects and diseases and in economics.

Thanks to a rapidly growing body of knowledge gained through years of research and experience, we now know with reasonable certainty how to establish and grow high quality black walnut crops. Even so, many specific problems remain to be solved before we can prescribe all the major steps in a technical system for walnut management on a wide range of sites.

Black walnut culture in recorded history began a few years after colonization. Rebmann (1907)[1] places its introduction into Europe about 1629. There are several citations in early European forestry literature of American walnut plantings. A natural hybrid between black walnut and Persian walnut was reported in France more than 150 years ago. There has been a continuing interest in black walnut introduction and culture in Europe for several years, but commercial walnut culture in Europe is usually limited to *Juglans regia*. A large black walnut plantation was recently established for timber production in Australia. Although the species has been planted in other countries for several hundred years, eastern United States and parts of adjacent Canada remain the primary commercial source of black walnut timber.

In North America the value of the wood was recognized soon after settlement. Walnut timber entered early Colonial commerce, and was a popular cabinet wood. I suspect that the earliest conscious cultural practice was to leave walnut trees on land cleared for pastures. This several-hundred-year-old practice likely developed because someone observed that such trees provided a convenient supply of nuts plus useful shade for livestock without greatly reducing forage production. This same practice is still followed in many parts of the country, and owners now recognize the added value of timber production. Favoring walnut trees in pastures thus has a significant impact on commercial timber and nut supplies. This practice is not to be confused with running cattle in woodlands, which is not recommended in central hardwoods.

When the settlers moved from clearings in heavily wooded areas to the prairies, they hated to give up their walnut trees. So they — maybe at the insistence of the women — took walnuts with them into the eastern prairies. Again, I suggest that the primary reason was for nuts although lumber for furniture and shade for the farmstead made walnut a popular multi-purpose tree beginning about 1850. Farmers who learned to crop the prairies instinctively knew that in order to grow trees on the prairie you must control weeds and grass. Walnut groves became part of the prairie landscape in Illinois, Iowa, and adjacent States. Here is how Mr. D. C. Scofield of Elgin, Illinois, recommended establishing walnut, based on his experience beginning in 1858: "These facts lead to the conclusion that black walnut will succeed on dry, rich soil if cultivation is continued till the trees are able to shade out grass..." (Hough 1877).[2]

---

[1] *Rebmann. Transactions of the German Dendrological Society, 1907. p. 187-209. 1907.*

[2] *F. B. Hough. Report upon forestry. U.S. Dep. Agric. 650 p. 1877.*

There is strong similarity between the foregoing prescription and the planting systems developed during the past few years. The big difference is the use of herbicides, but the basic ingredient is the same: control of weeds and grass. Like the principles of Mendel, the early prescription for establishing the prairie plantations was lost. Emphasis on mass production, cost-cutting methods that prevail even today replaced the know-how developed through early practical experience.

Although initial establishment was good, the low quality of individual trees in walnut groves shows that culture did not extend beyond the establishment period. Excessive grazing, fire, and lack of pruning resulted in poor quality trees that were avoided by the veneer industry until 10 to 15 years ago. Most of the old walnut groves have now been harvested for domestic and foreign consumption even though there have been problems of quality relating mainly to persistent branches. However, the harvest of walnut groves has proved emphatically that black walnut can be grown successfully in pure plantations if agronomic practices are followed.

The basis for the current recommendations for planting and caring for walnut has evolved from many years of research and experience. Research was somewhat sporadic from the 1930's until about 1960. During this period, interest in walnut culture was relatively modest, sustained primarily by programs of the American Walnut Manufacturers Association and a few zealous extension foresters and State foresters. Since 1960 there has been a steady increase in the interest in walnut culture. Unquestionably, this interest coincided with higher prices being offered for quality timber.

Because of the combined efforts of many individuals, industry, and public agencies, we can now prescribe with some certainty how to establish plantations and how to culture immature trees. Better technical information, especially for plantation establishment, has increased interest in walnut. Site evaluation has improved. Seed can be stored for several years and better seedlings are being produced in the nursery. Using large, well balanced seedlings, we can plant by any one of several methods if basic principles are followed. Then with either mechanical or chemical weed control, survival in excess of 80 percent can be expected routinely.

We are beginning to learn how to shape the trees during the first few years after planting, but early

form remains a serious problem. Some guides have been developed for pruning both planted and natural trees for clear wood production. We know something about plantation spacing and mixed plantings. Pole-sized trees in natural stands were found to respond well to release.

Thus, through new knowledge, significant progress has been made to improve field practices during the past 10 years. Interest in special walnut cost-sharing programs for planting, release, and pruning is growing rapidly in many States. Even so, efforts should be redoubled to get greater participation in cost-sharing not only for walnut but for other forestry practices. Walnut stock production in State nurseries has increased four-fold since 1963 and the quality of the seedlings has improved. More important, Cooperative Forest Management foresters are requiring and getting better jobs done under cost-sharing. More and better technical information is available to the forester and the grower. A key factor in the recent improvement in cultural practices surely has been the intensive training efforts being made by various university extension specialists, State organizations, industry, and the Northeastern Area of State and Private Forestry of the Forest Service. More recently the Walnut Council has become a significant factor in promoting the culture of walnut.

Good progress has been made in solving problems in walnut culture, but it does not take the walnut expert long to run out of specific answers. We still must do too much generalizing in a number of specialized areas. Positive evaluations are needed to define the potentials for a wider range of walnut sites, especially on the medium-to-poor sites. A good start has been made on fertilization research; some early results are promising but others are erratic. In some years, many States find it difficult to obtain adequate seed for nursery stock production. The few seed production areas established will produce only a fraction of our total needs. Some refinements are needed in nursery production and seed handling, and all nurserymen are not convinced that larger seedlings are best or that the advantages are worth the added cost. We are not yet able to produce the kind of seedling or develop the conditions needed to get rapid growth the first year after planting. And planters need to be aware that improved plant material may need special treatment when and if it becomes available.

Further refinements are needed for corrective pruning. We do not know how early to start pruning for clearwood production, and we have not determined for all ages and sizes the optimum amount of crown to remove at one time without reducing growth or quality. The optimum amount of growing space individual trees need at different ages in natural stands or in plantations has not been determined. Industry has expressed concern about the sapwood-heartwood ratio of fast-growing planted trees.

Better information is essential to establish thinning schedules and regulate spacing throughout the life of walnut stands on different sites. Closely related to the subject of spacing is the topic of multiple cropping. A good start has been made, but yield and quality data are needed for wood, grass, and nuts.

We have a good story to tell about how well black walnut is suited to intensive culture. Many landowners and foresters are convinced that the high prices paid for quality trees is reason enough to plant and tend walnut crops. Unfortunately, essential questions about economics and potentially disastrous pests remain unanswered. It is time to get down to business and develop an operational system on an economic basis. All of the costs and how to reduce them must be considered. And we need to consider all of the benefits — esthetics as well as timber, nut, and grass production.

SELECTING THE BEST AVAILABLE SOILS

Craig K. Losche, *Soil Scientist*
Forestry Sciences Laboratory, North Central Forest Experiment Station
Carbondale, Illinois [1]

ABSTRACT.—The relationship between observable soil characteristics and black walnut growth is discussed, and a procedure presented for using soil and topographic factors to select and evaluate areas for growing black walnut. Also, the influence of soil characteristics on the need for and extent of various cultural practices is examined.

One of the most important decisions the black walnut grower makes is selecting the area to grow this valuable timber and nut-producing hardwood. Growing a crop of high-value walnut trees is a long-term project that requires investments for planting, weed control, shaping, and pruning. Cultural practices could prove ineffective if the trees do not respond because of unsuitable soil conditions on the site. Or the grower's investment could be lost if the walnuts die. The grower should remember that a few extra minutes spent initially in evaluating the soil may mean the difference between success and failure.

This paper summarizes the soil characteristics that influence walnut growth, tells how to select the best available soils, and explains how soil characteristics influence the use of cultural practices.

SOIL CHARACTERISTICS INFLUENCING GROWTH

In the proceedings of the 1966 Black Walnut Workshop, Carmean (1966) reviewed the literature pertinent to the soil-site relations of this valuable hardwood. He indicated that there had been few studies of walnut site requirements and that only general estimates of site quality could be made. About all that was known was that better growth occurs on deep, well-drained soils with a medium texture and a loose, permeable subsoil, and that shallow, heavy-textured, or imperfectly drained soils are not suitable for walnut. Attempts to associate

soil chemical properties had not yielded conclusive information relating soil reaction and nutrients to better growth of walnut. Carmean described the height-growth pattern of five black walnut trees growing in 25- to 30-year-old plantations. The initial height growth was generally rapid, even on the poor sites, but the height-growth pattern varied widely after this period.

On the basis of later research, Carmean (1970) reported that the height-growth patterns of walnut are related to certain soil conditions. Losche (1970) found that the internal soil drainage of a site influences walnut height and diameter growth. Growth tended to be greater as the depth to mottling (evidence of restricted internal drainage) increased. Diameter growth was about 2.6 inches greater in 25 years on well-drained soils (30 inches or more to mottling) than on imperfectly drained soils (6 to 30 inches to mottling).

A study of walnut plantations in southern Illinois showed that the presence of a gravel layer was the key soil characteristic affecting growth on narrow floodplains. After 25 years, trees were 17 feet taller and 2.5 inches greater in diameter on deep soils (more than 40 inches to gravel) than on shallow soils (gravel within 40 inches of surface). The faster height growth on deep soils would increase the possibility of harvesting a second 16-foot log or developing a larger crown for nut production. If this diameter-growth pattern continues, the time to produce a merchantable 16-inch log will be reduced from 100 years to about 60 years.

Depth to mottling or gravel effectively limits the rooting zone from which moisture and nutrients must be obtained. Although these studies did not include soils

---

[1] *The Station's laboratory in Carbondale is maintained in cooperation with Southern Illinois University.*

with hardpans, claypans, fragipans, or other root-inhibiting features, walnut growth would likely be reduced on these soils also.

SELECTING THE BEST AVAILABLE SOILS

A grower's initial concern should be to select from the available areas those best suited for walnut. Research has shown that he will have to make investments for early cultural care in order to get a successful plantation; therefore, he will want to be sure that the proposed area will sustain rapid growth from planting to maturity.

The grower may examine the soils himself or seek the assistance of the local service or extension forester serving his area. In either case, the service forester should be contacted to obtain the latest information on weed control, pruning, and all other aspects of walnut culture.

For the "do-it-yourself" grower, the following topographic and soil characteristics should be looked for and evaluated at each potential area. By selecting the area with the least number of factors that would limit walnut growth, the grower will have selected the best available area on his land.

A. Topographic Factors:

(1) *Smooth and gently rolling landscapes.* — Site position is not generally a critical factor in these areas. Soil characteristics, such as texture and internal drainage, are most important.

(2) *Strongly rolling and mountainous landscapes.* — Site position and slope aspect, as well as soil characteristics, are very important in site selection. The better planting areas are typically located on the lower north- and east-facing slopes, stream terraces, and floodplains. Steep, south-facing slopes and narrow ridgetops would generally be poor walnut sites.

B. Soil Characteristics:[2]

(1) *Texture.* — Suitable soils have a sandy loam, loam, or silt loam topsoil texture; the subsoil should have the same texture or a sandy clay loam or clay loam. Soils with coarse sand or gravel layers and bedrock with-

in 2 to 3 feet of surface should be avoided, as should soils with acid, clayey subsoils. Limestone soils with silt loam over clayey subsoil are good planting sites.

(2) *Internal drainage.* — Soils with a uniform brown, yellowish- or reddish-brown color to 3 feet or more are well-drained. Soils with evidence of mottling within 2 feet of the surface should be avoided. Mottling refers to the color pattern of a soil with restricted (slow) internal drainage. A soil with red, yellow, or gray spots (blotches) or a uniform gray color indicates slow internal drainage.

When requested, a State service forester will examine your land with these characteristics in mind, and he will also have some experience with how well walnut grows on the local soils. He will also know how to obtain and interpret soil survey information and have technical guides[3] available to aid in selecting the best available land.

SOIL CHARACTERISTICS INFLUENCING CULTURAL PRACTICES

The growth response to most cultural practices will be directly or indirectly influenced by soil characteristics. For example, the effectiveness of early weed control treatments using pre-emergence herbicides depends on using the appropriate rate of chemical; this varies with soil texture, reaction (pH), and organic matter content. The rate necessary generally is higher as soil texture becomes finer, as pH increases, and as organic matter content increases. Silvicultural operations such as weeding and thinning indirectly affect the soil moisture and nutrient supply by reserving the soil's limited natural supply for the crop trees, especially on droughty and infertile soils.

Especially during the establishment period of a plantation, the grower will use practices similar to those of a

---

[2] *Dig a soil pit or use a soil auger and check soil characteristics to at least 3 feet.*

[3] *For example: "Guide to the Selection of Soil Suitable for Growing Black Walnut in Illinois," by C. K. Losche, W. M. Clark, E. E. Voss, and B. S. Ashley. Special Publication, Northeastern Area, State and Private Forestry, USDA Forest Service, Upper Darby, Pennsylvania. 1972. (Cooperative publication of the Forest Service and Soil Conservation Service.) Similar technical guides are available in all States from local service foresters and Soil Conservation Service personnel.*

row-crop farmer. Like the farmer, the walnut grower has made a substantial investment when establishing a plantation; therefore, he must protect his investment by selecting the best available soil and by planning his cultural practices with regard to the soil characteristics of the area selected.

LITERATURE CITED

Carmean, Willard H. 1966. Soil and water requirements. *In* Black Walnut Culture, p. 32-34, illus. USDA For. Serv., North Cent. For. Exp. Stn., St. Paul, Minn.

Carmean, Willard H. 1970. Tree height-growth patterns in relation to soil and site. *In* Tree Growth and Forest Soils. 499-512, illus. Third North Am. For. Soils Conf. Proc., Aug. 1968.

Losche, Craig K. [n.d. circa 1970]. Walnut site selection and soil management. Northeast. Area Nurserymen's Conf. Proc., Carbondale, Ill., Aug. 20-21, 1969: 55-58.

ESTABLISHMENT AND EARLY CULTURE
OF PLANTATIONS

Robert D. Burke, *Forester*
Pierson-Hollowell Company, Inc.
Martinsville, Indiana

and

Robert D. Williams, *Silviculturist*
Forestry Sciences Laboratory, North Central Forest Experiment Station
Carbondale, Illinois [1]

ABSTRACT.—Presented is a summary of information needed to establish and care for black walnut plantations. Subjects discussed include: how to choose a planting site, spacing, seedling selection and care, when and how to plant seedlings or seed, benefits from interplanted species, the need for and how to control weeds, when and how to prune to promote apical dominance, and clear stem pruning.

INTRODUCTION

Since the 1966 Walnut Workshop much interest has been generated in growing black walnut. News of the high prices paid for some walnut trees has probably created more interest than any other factor. People are demonstrating increased interest in walnut by planting trees. In 1971 about four times as many walnut seedlings were planted as in 1963. The increased interest in walnut planting will likely continue. Our research and experience in establishing successful walnut plantations during the past several years is summarized here and may prove helpful to new growers.

SITE SELECTION

Site selection is the most important step in establishing a walnut plantation. Walnut plantations should never be established without a knowledge of the soils. Soils are difficult to understand, so an expert should be consulted to determine soil capabilities for good tree growth.

For continued good growth walnut trees need deep, well-drained soils. Although the minimum soil depth recommended for growing black walnut is from 30 to 40 inches, trees will penetrate a much greater depth of available soil. One 9-year-old walnut tree had an excavated tap root about 7½ feet long and lateral roots 8

---

[1] *The Station's laboratory in Carbondale is maintained in cooperation with Southern Illinois University.*

feet long (fig. 1). Often potential sites appear good on the surface but are undesirable because of various root restrictions. Fragipans, high water tables, and shallow soils — either to bedrock or to gravel (especially fields along stream bottoms) — are examples of barriers that restrict root growth.

Brushy areas and cleared forest sites can be excellent for growing walnut. However, herbicide treatment of all stumps is imperative to prevent sprouting.[2] Pasture areas, and fields previously under cultivation, are good walnut planting sites, too, if the soils are deep, well-drained, and not too badly degraded.

SPACING

Spacing should be wide enough to accommodate the equipment that will be used in the plantation. Most farm equipment can easily move between rows planted on an 11- by 11-foot spacing and will cause little damage to the trees if the operator is careful. Checked rows permit cultivating and mowing in four directions (fig. 2). Also, in checked plantations a lone tractor operator, by using boom sprayers, can simultaneously spot spray herbicide at the base of individual trees in two rows. In unchecked plantations only one row can be sprayed. Although the initial cost of establishing a checked plantation is high because of the time required for layout, a large checked plantation may provide tremendous savings in long-term labor costs.

---

[2] *See page 114.*

Figure 1. — *The tap root of this 9-year-old walnut tree is about 7½ feet long and the lateral roots extend more than 8 feet from the tap root.*

SEEDLING SELECTION AND CARE

Only large, vigorous, well-balanced walnut seedlings should be planted. Seedlings ¼-inch or larger in diameter, measure above the root collar, survive better and grow faster than smaller ones and should be used (Williams 1970). Based on results of one study, root fibrosity does not affect either survival or early growth (Williams 1972). Roots may be pruned to 8 to 10 inches. Only the large, vigorous seedlings have been planted in company plantations and survival has been 98 percent.

Seedlings that cannot be planted for 1 or 2 weeks after they are received from the nursery should be heeled-in or placed in cold storage until planted. Walnut seedlings that will be planted in a few days may be left in the bundles if stored in a cool, moist, shady place.

PLANTING METHODS

Dormant seedlings should be planted in the spring anytime after the frost is out of the ground. Spring planting is more successful than fall planting because many fall-planted seedlings will frost heave.

Several planting methods are suitable for planting walnut seedlings. The KBC planting bar and a 6-inch post-hole auger, mounted on a chain saw engine, are two good methods (fig. 3). Planting machines can be used, too, but care must be taken to ensure that the seedlings are planted deep enough and straight. All seedlings should be checked after they are planted to make sure they are upright. Slanted trees should be straightened with a spade or planting bar.

Figure 2. — *Walnut rows in Pierson-Hollowell plantings are checked on an 11- by 11-foot spacing to allow cultivation in four directions.*

Regardless of the planting method used, the root collar of the seedlings should be planted 1 or 2 inches below the ground line. The hole or slit should be large enough and deep enough to accommodate the entire root system. Then with the seedling held upright, the soil should be firmly pressed around the roots to eliminate air pockets. Roots of walnut seedlings taken to the field should be kept in wet peat moss or some other suitable material to prevent the roots from drying.

Although planting walnut seedlings has proven to be the best method for establishing plantations, seed (nuts) can be planted, too. However, because rodents, especially squirrels, pilfer the seed, direct seeding has been very disappointing. Several methods have been tried in order to protect the nuts. Some of the more effective ones have been the tin can method and cones or cylinders constructed from screen wire or hardware cloth. Tin cans should be burned to hasten decomposition. An emergence hole is then punched in the closed end so that the jagged edges of the hole protrudes to the outside. The can is then filled with soil so that the enclosed nut will be planted 1-inch below the emergence hole when the can is placed in the ground, emergence hole up. Cones or cylinders must be buried 2 to 3 inches and

anchored to prevent the rodents from digging under them. Planting nuts could reduce plantation establishment costs tremendously if the problem of rodents could be solved. More research should be done in this area.

Low germination has been another problem confronting direct seeding enthusiasts, but planting germinated nuts could eliminate this problem. In the spring, after fall-collected seed has been in outside or cold room stratification at least 90 days, the seed should be placed in an environment suitable for germination (warm — about 70° F. and moist). Because the nuts should be planted before the radicle becomes long enough to be broken easily, the nuts should be inspected every second or third day to remove germinants. Germinated nuts should be planted immediately but may be held a few days in cold storage before planting.

On a limited basis we have planted container-grown seedlings and tubelings. Survival and growth of container-grown seedlings were excellent but the difficulties in handling and transporting container-grown seedlings would be too difficult for large-scale planting. Our experience with tubelings was disappointing. Neither survival nor growth was improved over bare root seedlings.

Figure 3. — *A 6-inch diameter planting hole being dug with a chain saw post-hole auger.*

INTERPLANTINGS

Several species have been interplanted in studies to: (1) force walnut height growth, (2) hasten natural pruning, (3) provide wind protection, and/or (4) provide nitrogen fixation. Some fast growing species should not be interplanted until the walnut is in its second or third growing season. There should be no danger of the interplanted species interfering with the growth of the walnut. We have interplanted white ash, white pine, autumn olive, black locust, and European alder. All species mentioned will force walnut height growth, cause natural pruning, and provide some wind protection.

The importance of wind protection should not be overlooked. Excessive transpiration rates and mechanical leaf injury were caused by wind movement (Schneider, *et al.* 1968). In Pierson-Hollowell plantations the best growth has occurred on trees located in areas where some wind protection has been provided. In the future,

company plantations that need wind protection will be interplanted before the second or third growing season. More research is needed on wind protection of sapling-size walnut plantations.

To date European alder appears to be the best interplanting species in the Pierson-Hollowell plantations. In addition to wind protection, pruning, and forcing faster height growth, European alder, in association with root nodules, fixes nitrogen in the soil that may be utilized by the walnut. Where European alder has been interplanted in our plantations, growth of the walnut has been excellent. After 5 years the European alder is slightly taller than the walnut (fig. 4). If the walnut cannot compete, the European alder should be topped but not removed so it can continue to fix nitrogen and provide natural pruning. We believe that interplanted trees will greatly reduce pruning costs.

WEED CONTROL

Weeds and grasses must be controlled around each walnut seedling the first few years to increase survival and promote faster growth. Weed control is second in importance only to site selection in establishing walnut plantations. In addition to better survival and faster growth, weed control reduces rodent damage by eliminating their cover. Herbicides control weeds and grasses best but competing vegetation can be controlled by cultivation, too. However, seedlings can be damaged when equipment is used too close to the seedling. Cultivation is very effective between the rows to supplement spot or strip herbicide treatment around the seedlings (fig. 2). However, if all vegetation is controlled either by herbicides, mechanical cultivation, or a combination of the two, erosion becomes a serious problem, especially on sloping lands. An excellent combination treatment is to use herbicides around the seedlings and mow between the rows. Unless the weeds are tall and very dense, mowing may not be necessary. However, rabbits cut off small seedlings and field mice and groundhogs damage seedlings by chewing on the bark. These animal problems can be reduced or eliminated by cultivating or mowing between the rows to eliminate cover.

Strip spraying along the rows is an effective means of weed control. Strip spraying may be used in interplantings where spacing within the rows is too close to permit cross mowing or cultivating.

CORRECTIVE PRUNING

Corrective pruning during the first few years of the walnut plantation is a necessary expense. *Before* plant-

Figure 4. — *A 5-year-old walnut tree (center foreground) trained and nourished by 4-year-old interplanted European alder (right foreground) which is slightly taller than the walnut.*

ing it may be necessary to prune broken or damaged stems. Stems damaged or broken *during* planting should be pruned immediately. Either time, all damaged stem should be cut off above a live bud. Removing this damaged stem can reduce the incidence of slanted or multiple stems.

Severe spring frost may kill part or all of the new growth. Frost damage in new plantations necessitates a pruning expense. Frost damage will continue to be a problem unless a way is found to prevent it, or unless frost-hardy seedlings are produced through genetic selection. How to prevent frost damage is another major problem on which we should focus more research.

A new, very effective technique for correcting forked or multiple stemmed trees is "tape pruning" (Bey 1973). The technique requires that trees be pruned in the spring just before growth starts. Timing is important because the tape deteriorates in 2 to 3 months and must be in place during the rapid growth period. Two or more stems of a tree with multiple leaders should be drawn together to straighten the selected leader. Wrap the area where the stems cross 3 to 6 times with 1-inch masking tape. Then clip the tips of all but the selected leader above the tape. With few exceptions, trials of this method in 1971 and 1972 resulted in single, straight stems.

Black walnut has the unique ability to sprout after being damaged by frost, chemicals, machinery, wind, or insects. Normally trees will sprout within 2 or 3 weeks if damaged during the growing season. Trees should be correctively pruned as soon as it is possible to choose the best stem. If several new shoots appear, all except the largest, most upright should be removed.

During the summer of 1970, the periodical cicada or 17-year locust did extensive damage to 1- to 2-year-old walnut plantations in Indiana. In a planting near Richmond, Indiana, all damaged seedlings were coppiced (stem cut 1 to 2 inches above the ground) before the 1971 growing season. Most of the coppiced seedlings sprouted and looked very healthy during the 1971 growing season. Coppicing is an effective method for correcting extensive damage to small walnut trees (less than 3 inches in diameter). Because of potential heart rot, coppicing should be used only as a last resort on trees larger than 3 inches.

Dieback sometimes occurs in 1-year-old plantations. This problem is probably due to poor transplanting stock or improper care of the seedlings before planting. Do not become impatient and replace these apparently dead seedlings until it is obvious that they are dead. The root system of many may still be alive and a new sprout will develop. If dieback occurs, a firm upward pull on the stem will determine if the root system is dead or alive. A dead root system will slip out of the ground while a live root system will hold.

CLEAR STEM PRUNING

To produce a stem free of knots it is necessary to remove a few lower branches periodically as the walnut tree increases in height until 17 feet of bole are limb free. An adequate crown is needed to produce good growth so don't remove lower branches too fast. At least half the total tree height should be in live crown. Removing too many limbs from young trees could concentrate too much growth at the terminal and cause the tree to bend over under its own weight.

Equipment striking side branches and breaking or tearing them from the stem is a serious problem. A pruning technique has been used in Pierson-Hollowell plantings that has reduced the damage caused by equipment to seedlings and saplings. Lower branches are sheared during the dormant season, leaving 8- to 10-inch stubs. Shearing has several advantages: (1) There are no branches to damage in *early* spring when important cultural practices such as spraying, cultivation, and mowing are performed. (2) There is only a slight increase in the diameter of the stub left on the stem (a normal branch will about double in diameter). (3) Shearing forces height growth in early spring, but later, lateral buds form new branches on the stubs bringing the tree into balance. (4) If equipment strikes the limb, only the new growth (which originates on the stub) will be torn off, leaving the main stem intact.

FERTILIZING PLANTATIONS

Walnut plantations established on the proper soils will receive sufficient nutrients for good growth. Indiscriminate use of fertilizers may depress seedling growth by stimulating competing weed growth.

Fertilizer tablets (20-10-5) were placed in 1,000 planting holes in a 1968 company plantation. Five years after planting the fertilized seedlings were not growing any faster than the unfertilized seedlings. In 1970 tablets were placed in 1,400 more planting holes. The first growing season the leaves were deeper green than the unfertilized seedlings, but there was no difference in diameter or height growth.

CONCLUSIONS

Walnut has a high potential value and appears to be a desirable investment. But unless the necessary weed control and corrective pruning are done when needed, walnut growth would be slow and the crooked, limby trees would be of little monetary value.

Before planting walnut the land manager should provide for the weed control necessary for fast, early growth and the corrective pruning and clear stem pruning needed to produce valuable lumber and veneer logs.

LITERATURE CITED

Bey, Calvin F. 1973. Corrective pruning young black walnut trees — a new twist. North. Nut Grow. Assoc. Proc., Ames, Iowa, Aug. 21, 1972. (In press.)

Schneider, Gary, Ghaus Khattak, and John Bright. 1968. Modifying site for the establishment of black walnut. North Am. For. Soils Conf. Proc. 3: 155-169.

Williams, Robert D. 1970. Planting large black walnut seedlings on cultivated sites. USDA For. Serv. Tree Plant. Notes 21(2): 13-14, illus.

Williams, Robert D. 1972. Root fibrosity proves insignificant in survival, growth of black walnut seedlings. USDA For. Serv. Tree Plant. Notes 23(3): 22-25, illus.

WEED CONTROL

W. R. Byrnes, *Professor*
Department of Forestry and Conservation
Purdue University
Lafayette, Indiana

J. E. Krajicek, *Associate Silviculturist*
Forestry Sciences Laboratory
North Central Forest Experiment Station
Carbondale, Illinois

J. R. Wichman, *Graduate Instructor in Research*
Department of Forestry and Conservation
Purdue University
Lafayette, Indiana

ABSTRACT.—Weeds are unwanted plants that seriously compete with young black walnut for essential growth factors — space, light, moisture, and nutrients. Weed control is very important in plantations to assure successful establishment and early growth of walnut. Mechanical or chemical methods are feasible for weed control; but chemical control with pre- or postemergence herbicides is normally more effective and economical. Herbicides can be applied broadcast over entire areas or restricted to strips or spots adjacent to planted trees. Users of herbicides should be familiar with herbicide regulations and strictly adhere to precautions and directions listed on the label.

Weed control is important in the early years of black walnut (*Juglans nigra* L.) establishment and growth. Weed competition is especially critical in walnut plantations, because they are usually established on good sites in full sunlight — ideal conditions for vigorous growth of many types of weeds. Under these conditions, weed species may compete with black walnut for space, light, moisture, and nutrients. These environmental factors are essential for optimum growth and development of black walnut, at least in its early years.

Weed competition can result in reduced growth and vigor or mortality of young trees. It may cause physical deformities that reduce walnut merchantability and quality. Weeds also can provide habitat for rodents that may girdle or even cut off the planted seedlings (Byrnes 1966). Monetary losses attributable to lack of weed control in tree culture have not been determined. However, in agricultural production direct losses due to weeds have been estimated to exceed $5 billion annually (U.S. Department of Agriculture 1965).

Weeds simply are plants growing where they are not wanted. For our purposes, they can be classified into two broad groups: (1) *woody species,* including trees, shrubs, and vines and (2) *herbaceous species,* including grasses, sedges, and broadleaved plants. It is important to assess the kind of weed problem existing on a given area and even to recognize individual weed species. The weed species present, their stage of growth, and existing soil characteristics need to be identified in order to apply the most effective, efficient, and economical weed control methods.

WEED CONTROL METHODS

Weed control in walnut culture may be needed prior to or after plantations are established, or in natural stands. The need for site preparation will depend on the competition present. Problem weeds present may be controlled by mechanical or chemical methods as described at the first walnut workshop (Byrnes 1966).

Previously recommended chemical methods are still effective in black walnut culture. However, some herbicides have been restricted for certain uses by Federal and State agencies. Users of these materials should familiarize themselves with their local and State regulations by contacting county agricultural agents, extension specialists, and service foresters. Also, always read the label, heed precautions, and follow directions when using an herbicide (see page 114).

Two major herbicides that have been used for weed control in black walnut production are now under new regulations. These are 2,4,5-T and amitrole. Both are prohibited by the Environmental Protection Agency for use on cropland or food crops, but their use is not affected for other purposes, except around homes and waters. These two chemicals are not presently registered for black walnut, because black walnut nuts are considered a food crop. Future regulations of these chemicals, especially 2,4,5-T, are pending the outcome of public hearings by the Environmental Protection Agency. Implementation of new legislation under the Federal Environmental Pesticide Control Act of 1972 (U.S. Congress 1972) undoubtedly will result in close regulation of some herbicides at the Federal and State level; and further, it is probable that some herbicides will be restricted to use by certified applicators. With these developments, we are truly in the era of prescription weed control.

Plantation Weed Control

Weed control in young walnut plantations is most important. Heavy sod and/or dense stands of herbaceous weeds seriously interfere with seedling establishment. Mechanical, chemical, or combined methods can be used to achieve the desired control in preplanting or postplanting treatments. Though complete eradication of weeds may be desirable, it is not always practical or feasible.

Mechanical Control

Cultivation can be used to destroy existing vegetation and prepare the site for planting. After the plantation is established, cultivation, mowing, or mulching may be used. Mechanical control involves more work and is usually more expensive than chemical control. However, if the landowner has equipment and labor available, mechanical methods may be the best alternative.

Mowing controls weed competition for space and light. It may favor changes in species composition to low-growing biennial and perennial weeds that compete with planted trees for moisture and nutrient elements. Weeds should be mowed as close to the trees as possible. Repeated followup treatments are needed during the growing season. On moist, fertile sites, mowing may be an entirely satisfactory weed control method, if done frequently.

Cultivation is the most practical mechanical means of controlling weeds. A rotary tiller or disc harrow is customarily used. Cultivation should be repeated as often as necessary to keep weeds from getting over 6 inches tall. Care should be exercised to avoid damage to shallow feeder roots of walnut trees. When using cultivation or mowing equipment in the plantation, special care must be taken to avoid injuries to walnut stems that could result in physical deformities or provide entry sites for insects and disease.

Mulching is practical only in small plantings. A 4-foot square of black plastic film can be split, placed around a tree, and anchored to the ground. However, plastic will sometimes cause heat-girdling damage and may provide cover for mice that could damage roots and lower stems. Sawdust and wood chips can also be used as mulch, but existing vegetation should be removed before mulch is applied.

Chemical Methods

Two general types of herbicides are effective for controlling grasses and broadleaf weeds. These are (1) pre-emergence, soil-applied chemicals, which are applied from late fall to early spring on unfrozen soil before weeds emerge and (2) postemergence chemicals, which are applied to the foliage of established weeds.

Pre-emergence herbicides are not very effective on established weeds. If advanced weed growth is already present on the planting site, application of a postemergence herbicide is advisable. Where herbicide application is delayed until spring or early summer, a combination of postemergence and pre-emergence herbicides can be used to kill established weeds and provide residual control of germinating weeds. All pre-emergence herbicides require rainfall or light tillage to incorporate the chemical into the soil, a good reason for treatment a week or so in advance of expected weed emergence. In established plantations, postemergence herbicides *must be used as directed sprays* to avoid damage to the planted trees.

Here are some herbicides for grass and broadleaf herbaceous weed control that we have used experimentally. Some of them are not registered for walnut:

1. *Simazine:* Simazine is a pre-emergence, soil-applied herbicide. It is absorbed by plant roots and translocated to the leaves, where it exerts its toxic effect. Black walnut has a fairly high tolerance for this chemical (Wichman and Byrnes 1971). Simazine normally remains in the upper soil surface due to absorption by clay and organic matter. At recommended rates, it effectively controls most newly germinated grasses and herbs for one growing season. It can be applied in late fall or early spring. Available formulations are 80 percent wettable powder (80W) and 4 percent granular (4G). The granular formulation is more costly for the same degree of weed control. Rates of application for tree species are listed on the label or may be obtained from county agricultural agents and extension specialists, since the rates suitable for good control in cornfields are usually adequate for control around walnut trees. General application rates are 2 to 4 pounds active ingredient per acre in a water carrier. If necessary, simazine can be sprayed over the tops of dormant walnut trees.

2. *Atrazine:* Atrazine is a pre-emergence, soil-applied herbicide closely related to simazine, but exhibits some postemergence activity. It may control emerged weeds if sprayed when they are less than 1½ inches tall. It moves deeper into the soil than simazine, making it more effective on deep-germinating weed species such as morning glory. Black walnut possesses some inherent tolerance for this chemical (Wichman and Byrnes 1971), but field tests have given some indication of a lower tolerance than for simazine. Atrazine 80 percent wettable powder is applied in spring at locally recommended rates. The chemical should not be sprayed on the walnut trees.

3. *Simazine + atrazine* in a mixture may be superior to either of these chemicals alone, for more kinds of weeds may be controlled, because atrazine penetrates more deeply into the soil. This combination is not available commercially. However, the sum of active ingredients should not exceed that for the chemicals applied separately.

4. *Amitrole + Simazine:* This mixture of a post- and pre-emergence herbicide was effective in tests on established weeds and also provided residual control of germinating weeds. In postplanting treatments, accidental spraying of planted trees must be avoided. Various ratios of the two components can be obtained by mixing as desired. However, Amizine,[1] a commercial dry powder formulation containing 15 percent amitrole and 45 percent simazine, is available and is normally applied at 7 pounds in 100 gallons of water per acre treated. Amizine has also been made available recently in liquid form containing 5.1 percent amitrole and 10.2 percent simazine, but application rates for black walnut have not been completely worked out for the product label.

5. *Dalapon:* Dalapon is normally used as a post-emergence grass killer. It effectively controls many perennial and annual grasses. A rate of 10 pounds of the commercial product per 100 gallons of water per acre has been used in research trials. It must not be sprayed directly on walnuts, and should be applied when grass is growing vigorously, but before formation of seed heads.

6. *2,4-D Amine:* This is a postemergence, foliage-applied herbicide that is effective on most broadleaf weeds. It normally is used prior to tree planting where broadleaf perennial weeds are abundant. It can be used as a postplanting treatment to control patches of perennial vines. Recommended rate is 1.5 pounds acid equivalent of an amine salt formulation per acre in a water solution. Effectiveness may be increased by the addition of a spreader-sticker or low-sudsing detergent. *Do not spray on or allow spray drift to get on the walnut trees.*

Mechanical-Chemical

When chemical treatment is limited to strips or spots in the plantation, it may be desirable to control weeds between the treated areas by mechanical means, either mowing or cultivation. This practice may further reduce competition for soil moisture and may prevent vines from spreading into treated areas. Chemical control in combination with mowing can effectively remove weeds adjacent to the trees and also minimize the erosion hazard on sloping land. If cultivation is used on intervening areas, it should be restricted to land that is not subject to serious erosion; however, cultivation may not have an economic advantage over total chemical control in this situation.

---

[1] *The identification and description of commercial products in this publication are solely for information purposes. Endorsement of any commercial product by the Department of Agriculture is not intended and must not be inferred.*

Herbicide Application

Methods of applying these chemicals will vary depending on size of area to be treated, terrain, equipment available, type of herbicide to be used, and size of walnut trees. Pre-emergence herbicides can be broadcast over the entire area, or applied in strips or spots. Broadcast applications are the most expensive in terms of chemical cost, whereas spot treatments are the cheapest and the most versatile. Broadcast sprays should not be used on sloping land as they increase the chance of erosion.

For strip spraying, the strips should be about as wide as the trees are tall, but not less than 4 feet. For spot control, the diameter of treated circles should be about equal to the height of the tree but never less than 4 feet (Krajicek and Phares 1971).

Equipment for applying chemicals ranges from boom sprayers suitable for treating large areas of smooth level land to backpack sprayers for smaller areas and on irregular terrain. Some way of continuously agitating the solution is necessary for some herbicides. Granular formulations can be applied with specially designed mechanical spreaders, hand-operated granule spreaders, or by hand.

Boom sprayers must be calibrated so that rates can be applied accurately. The major factors to consider in proper calibration are sprayer pressure, tractor speed, and nozzle height, spacing, and type. Instructions for calibration are usually available from county agricultural agents, extension specialists, or farm supply stores.

When applying herbicides with a backpack sprayer, it is useful to calibrate for small areas, since this type of sprayer is generally used for spot or strip treatments. Assuming 100 gallons of water will be used with 5 pounds of the chemical formulation per *treated* acre, 10 gallons containing ½ pound (8 ounces) of chemical would be adequate for ¹/₁₀ acre (4,356 square feet). For strip spraying of 4-, 6-, or 8-foot widths, 10 gallons of solution should cover 1,090, 725, or 545 lineal feet, respectively. For spot spraying, the 10 gallons of solution will treat the following numbers of trees (Krajicek and Phares 1971):

Tree height	Diameter of spot	Trees treated
(Feet)	*(Feet)*	*(Number)*
4	4	350
6	6	155
8	8	90

For hand applications of granular simazine to circular plots around trees, the only tools needed are a pail and a measuring spoon. The required volume of granules is uniformly distributed over the circular plot by hand. Granular simazine should be applied in fall or very early spring because rainfall is required to carry the chemical into the soil.

Continuing Weed Control

The number of years after plantation establishment that weed control measures should be continued will depend on site factors, plantation objectives, and economic considerations. In plantations managed primarily for nuts, weed control may be desirable for as long as the trees are in production. In plantings managed for timber, results to date show that weed control should be continued for at least 2 to 3 years (Krajicek and Williams 1971). From the standpoint of improved growth, weed control will likely benefit trees until competition among trees becomes a controlling factor of growth. The length of time required for black walnut to dominate a site will depend on such factors as available moisture and nutrient elements.

The type of weed control practiced may change with time. When the planted trees are well above the tallest weeds, complete control becomes less important. However, control of vines such as wild grape, wild hops, climbing buckwheat, and morning glory must be continued until the plantation canopy is dense enough to suppress the growth of these plants.

WALNUT RESPONSE TO WEED CONTROL — FIELD TRIALS

The beneficial effects of weed control on black walnut growth are evident in results of the following field experiments conducted by Purdue University and the North Central Forest Experiment Station.

Bottomland Sites — Purdue University

At Purdue University, two studies of walnut growth response to weed control on bottomland sandy loam to loam sites were initiated in 1963 and 1965. In both studies, 2-year-old seedlings were planted at a 10- by 10-foot spacing in a randomized complete block design with three replicates of the following weed control treatments: (1) none (no weed control), (2) mechanical (cultivation with rotary tiller), and (3) chemical (Amizine at 7 lb./acre). In the mechanical treatments, plots were cultivated three times per season for 3 years after planting in both studies. In the chemical treatments, Amizine was applied once each spring for 3 years after planting. In the 1963 study applications were restricted to milacre plots (6.6 feet square) around each tree. In the 1965 study the entire treatment areas were sprayed. Weed control treatments were discontinued after the third year, but survival and growth measurements have been made annually.

Survival and Growth — 1963 Test

Black walnut survival after 10 years was excellent, ranging from 85 percent on mechanically treated plots to 95 percent on chemically treated plots (table 1). Average height and diameter were best on the plots receiving total area cultivation and somewhat less on the chemically treated plots (table 1). Although areas with no weed control had 88 percent survival, tree growth was significantly lower than on areas with weed control. Growth response occurred in the second year after planting for trees receiving weed control, but was delayed until the fourth year for trees with no weed control (fig. 1). Although the rate of tree growth on the "no control" treatment was about equal to that on the treated areas in the past 7 years, total growth has been consistently less.

Survival and Growth — 1965 Test

Walnut survival after 8 years in the 1965 study was 89 percent with no weed control, 88 percent with chemical control, and 79 percent with mechanical control (table 2). In contrast to the 1963 study, average height and diameter were greater for trees on chemically treated plots than for trees on cultivated plots (table 2). Trees with no weed control grew little during the first 4 years after planting, and their average height in fall 1972 was considerably less than trees on plots where weed competition had been eliminated during the establishment period (fig. 2). It is interesting to note in both studies that black walnut survival ws good with no weed control and that these trees ultimately began a respectable growth rate. However, it is not likely that they will catch up with trees that had early release from weed competition.

Table 1. — *Average survival, height, and d.b.h. of black walnut 10 growing seasons after planting*[1]

Weed treatment	Survival	Height	D.b.h.
	Percent	Feet	Inches
None	88	10.1	1.4
Chemical[2]	95	14.5	2.2
Mechanical[3]	85	16.5	2.6

[1] Two-year-old seedlings planted in May 1963.

[2] Amizine at 7 lbs./A. applied to milacre plots around each tree in 1963, 1964, and 1965.

[3] Cultivation of total area with rotary tiller three times per season in 1963, 1964, and 1965.

Planting on Cleared Forest Sites — Kaskaskia Experimental Forest

In the future it will become increasingly necessary to plant black walnut on sites already forested with less desirable species. In Hardin County, Illinois, two small coves were cleared and planted to black walnut.

Treatments were (1) complete control of competing vegetation, (2) control of herbaceous vegetation only, (3) control of woody vegetation only, and (4) competition not controlled. For each of the first three treatments, annual, biennial, and triennial control was tested.

After five growing seasons, survival was excellent for all treatments, ranging from 94 to 100 percent. Average height (almost 11 feet) was best for annual complete control. Biennial and triennial complete control, and annual and biennial control of only herbaceous vegetation gave heights almost as good, however. Control of woody vegetation but leaving herbaceous was no better than the check, where average height was only about 4 feet.

Weed Control (Spot Size and Site Preparation), Indiana and Illinois

The use of spot weed control instead of broadcast treatments is gaining interest. Reduced erosion and pollution and lower costs are the main advantages. But the size of spots needed at various stages of tree development, and whether or not soil preparation is needed prior to initial chemical application are important considerations.

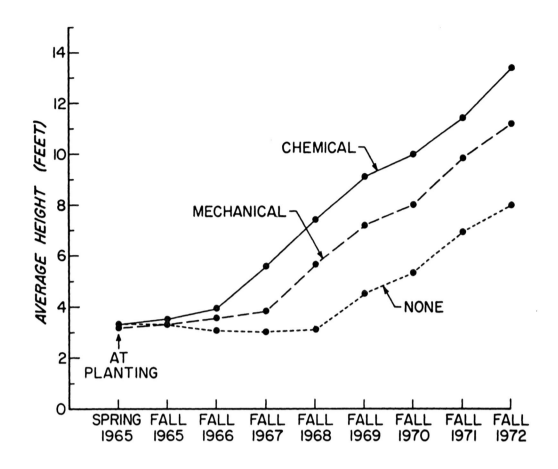

Figure 1. — *Average height of black walnut trees during 10 growing seasons by weed treatment — none, mechanical (cultivation over entire area in 1963, 1964, and 1965), and chemical (Amizine at 7 lbs./acre on milacre plots in 1963, 1964, and 1965).*

Table 2. — *Average survival, height, and d.b.h. of black walnut eight growing seasons after planting*[1]

Weed treatment	Survival	Height	D.b.h.
	Percent	Feet	Inches
None	89	8.0	0.9
Chemical[2]	88	13.4	2.0
Mechanical[3]	79	11.2	1.5

[1]/Two-year-old seedlings planted in April 1965.

[2]/Amizine at 7 lbs./A. over entire treatment area in 1965, 1966, and 1967.

[3]/Cultivation of total area with rotary tiller three times per season in 1965, 1966, and 1967.

The study was established on old-field sites on a bottomland area in south-central Indiana, an upland area in southern Illinois, and a bottomland site in southern Illinois. Both soil preparation and no preparation were tested on all areas. One-year-old black walnut seedlings and germinating nuts were used. Chemical weed control was applied after planting and sowing on circular spots 2, 4, 6, and 8 feet in diameter. On other areas, no weed control was used.

After two growing seasons, few differences in growth and survival are evident. However, it appears that a treated spot at least 4 feet in diameter is desirable. The most significant finding to date is that soil preparation prior to planting had no advantage over no preparation.

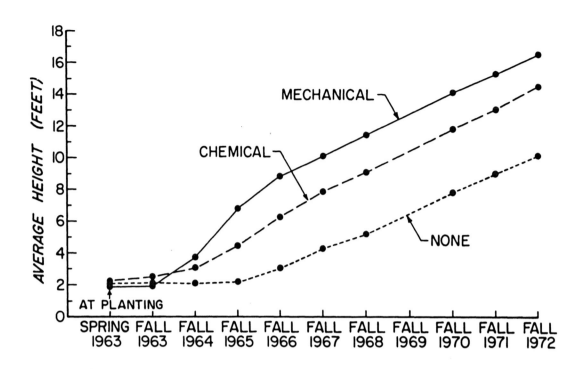

Figure 2. — *Average height of black walnut trees during eight growing seasons by weed treatment — none, mechanical (cultivation over entire area in 1965, 1966, and 1967), and chemical (Amizine at 7 lbs./acre over entire area in 1965, 1966, and 1967).*

This not only has economic implications but also indicates that areas not readily accessible to soil preparation equipment can be successfully planted.

LITERATURE CITED

Byrnes, W. R. 1966. Site preparation and weed control. *In* Black walnut culture, p. 20-27. North Cent. For. Exp. Stn., St. Paul, Minn.

Krajicek, John E., and Robert E. Phares. 1971. How to control weeds in black walnut plantings. USDA For. Serv., 8 p. North Cent. For. Exp. Stn., St. Paul, Minn.

Krajicek, John E., and Robert D. Williams. 1971. Continuing weed control benefits young planted black walnut. USDA For. Serv. Res. Note NC-122, 3 p. North Cent. For. Exp. Stn., St. Paul, Minn.

U.S. Department of Agriculture. 1965. Losses in agriculture. U.S. Dep. Agric., Agric. Handb. 291, 120 p.

U.S. Congress. 1972. Federal Environmental Pesticide Control Act of 1972. Public Law 92-516. Washington, D.C.: Government Printing Office.

Wichman, J. R., and W. R. Byrnes. 1971. Inherent tolerance of black walnut and yellow poplar seedlings to soil-applied herbicides. Purdue Univ. Agric. Exp. Stn., Res. Bull. 878, 4 p.

MANAGING IMMATURE TREES FOR MORE HIGH-QUALITY LOGS AND RELATED PRODUCTS

Robert E. Phares, *Principal Plant Physiologist*
Forestry Sciences Laboratory, North Central Forest Experiment Station
Carbondale, Illinois [1]

ABSTRACT.—A general review of some of the basic cultural practices in managing immature black walnut trees is presented. It is proposed that potential crop trees be selected as early in the rotation as possible and cultured on an individual tree basis. Early release and thinning are also recommended for maintaining rapid growth. Study results show that pole-sized and small sawtimber-sized walnut trees also grow faster if released and thinned, but older sawtimber-sized trees show little or no response. Tentative stocking and spacing levels for maintaining good growth and good nut production are presented. Corrective pruning and clear-stem pruning are necessary at appropriate times during the rotation to produce straight stems and high-quality wood. Research in progress indicates that fertilization also may be feasible for maintaining good growth.

Good walnut management must begin early in the life of a stand and continue through to final harvest to produce high yields and high-value products on short rotations. Too many walnut growers tend to ignore important management practices after a planting is established, or fail to recognize the advantages of managing naturally established trees. Much can be done with immature walnut trees to promote rapid growth of high-quality wood. Research and experience suggest that with proper care these immature trees can produce good seed crops in 10 to 12 years, 16-inch saw logs in 30 to 35 years, and 20-inch veneer logs in 40 to 50 years from the time of planting on good sites. And by applying some of these same practices to established trees, it is not unreasonable to expect that growth and quality can be more than doubled in only a few years. Without intensive management, growth and yield of immature trees will be lower and rotations longer.

Several basic cultural practices have widespread applicability to management of natural and planted walnut stands for a number of product objectives. Most landowners are primarily interested in growing walnut for high-value timber, but an increasing number are giving more attention to nut production and other aspects of walnut culture. Fortunately, the cultural practices currently recommended for growing high-quality timber generally do not conflict with those recommended for other product objectives. For example, good management of black walnut for high-quality timber also generally results in greater nut production. In this paper I will review some of these basic cultural practices and point out where new information has called for changes in emphasis or techniques.

SELECT POTENTIAL CROP TREES EARLY

Because of their high potential value, walnut trees should be managed on an individual basis, regardless of whether they are in plantations or in natural stands. Therefore, one of the first important tasks for the walnut grower is to select the best trees on which to concentrate wood production or improve nut production. The sooner these potential crop trees can be selected and favored with cultural treatments, the greater the total growth or yield and improvement in quality.

Generally there are fewer good potential crop trees in natural walnut stands than in plantations. Naturally established walnut trees are scattered and vary greatly in age, size, and form. In such cases, the grower must try to do what he can to improve growth and form of the trees available. In the denser stands, and in plantations, it is not practical to try to grow every tree to maturity; so the best trees should be selected at appropriate spacings and managed to improve their form and growth. From the economic viewpoint, it probably is more profitable to work with naturally established trees than to establish new plantations. Growers have minimal investments in the establishment of these trees, and the costs

[1] *The Station's laboratory at Carbondale is maintained in cooperation with Southern Illinois University.*

of cultural practices to speed up growth and improve quality do not have to be carried too long before the investments can be recovered.

Early growth characteristics often provide a good clue to future development. Therefore, potential crop trees can be selected in relatively young stands. Trees that are forked, have excessively large branches, or are defective for any other reason should not be selected as potential crop trees. Tall, clean-boled trees produce the best veneer logs, so straightness and cleanness of the bole are the best indicators of potential quality regardless of the age at which crop trees are selected. In older stands, the size of the crown and its relative position in the main canopy are good indicators of growth potential. When a choice is possible, dominant and codominant trees should be favored over intermediate and overtopped trees. Select the fastest growing trees as crop trees, using external characteristics such as bark pattern to evaluate current growth rate. The reddish-brown inner bark will be visible in the bark fissures on fast-growing trees. Slow-growing walnut trees tend to have flat, platy bark. Evidence of good nut production in previous years also may be helpful, especially if increased nut production is a major product objective. Trees that have fencing or signs nailed to them are poor candidates for veneer-log crop trees.

RELEASE AND THIN CROWDED TREES

Selected crop trees should have adequate growing space throughout most of the rotation to maintain rapid growth. If immature trees are crowded or overtopped, crown development and hence the potential for future growth will be seriously restricted. Early and frequent weeding will help keep the crowns above the competition and free to grow. Good site preparation during plantation establishment, especially on brushy fields or forested sites, will reduce the need for early weedings; however, some followup release is almost always needed to keep the walnut trees from being overtopped. Early release is best accomplished by cutting off competing brush and saplings during the dormant season and spraying the stumps with herbicides. Larger trees can be girdled or injected with herbicides. All vines should be removed from young crop trees because they can kill the branches and restrict crown development. Treating stumps of cut vines with herbicides will prevent resprouting.

The first thinning will probably not be needed until the trees reach sapling size (2 to 4 inches d.b.h.), but if the trees are growing in dense patches, an earlier thinning may be justified. Thinnings should be made every 8 to 10 years to remove slow-growing and poorly formed trees and provide more growing space to the better crop trees (fig. 1). Enough trees should be removed each time to allow the trees to grow about 4 inches in diameter before the crowns become too crowded and another thinning is needed. On most sites, this will mean that tree crowns should be 8 to 10 feet apart after each thinning.

Figure 1. — *This small sawtimber-sized walnut tree has had adequate growing space for several years. Consequently, it has produced a larger vigorous crown, and has good potential for high-value veneer log and nut production.*

The number of crop trees to leave per acre after each thinning, or the amount of growing space to provide each tree, varies with site quality, tree age or size, and product objective. Recommended stocking levels and spacing for high-quality veneer logs and good nut production on good sites are given in table 1. They are based on growing-space requirements of individual trees as determined in previous studies (Krajicek 1966), and on measurements of growth of individual trees in several spacing studies in progress. When nut production is a major product objective, fewer trees per acre should be grown to assure maximum crown development. If the crop trees are grown at the recommended stocking levels, only two or three noncommercial thinnings will be needed before some of the trees will be large enough to sell.

Growth can generally be stimulated by release and thinning even if these treatments are delayed several years, as observed in a number of 25- to 60-year-old walnut stands in southern Illinois and Indiana (table 2). The crop trees ranged from small poles to small sawtimber-sized trees and were growing on a wide range of site conditions. In each stand some of the crop trees were released, and some were not. After 5 years, many of the released trees were growing more than twice as fast as the unreleased trees. Growth response was closely correlated with increase in crown area.

In a similar study with 33-year-old pole-sized black walnuts on strip-mined soils in Kansas, low thinning and single-tree release were employed; diameter growth more than tripled after 2 years (Geyer and Naughton 1971). A strong correlation was found between the amount of crown growing space provided each tree and its diameter growth. Thus, thinning and release treatments must provide room for crown expansion if growth is to be increased.

If the crop trees are released and thinned adequately, growth should be stimulated for several years. An earlier study in Indiana showed that complete crown release doubled the growth of pole-sized black walnut for at least 8 years (Clark 1967, Phares and Williams 1971). A second light release after 8 years resulted in an additional growth increase (fig. 2). The duration of the growth response after release depends on how soon the tree crowns start crowding each other again.

Most pole-sized or larger stands of black walnut generally contain a heavy layer of understory vegetation, especially if they are fairly open and on good sites. This understory vegetation undoubtedly competes with the crop trees for moisture and nutrients, but it may not be practical to control this competition. Removal of understory vegetation from around half of the crop trees in each of the stands studied in southern Illinois and Indi-

Table 1. — *Tentative stocking guidelines for growing high-quality black walnut on good sites*

Average stand d.b.h. (inches)	Stocking and spacing when crowns begin to touch[1]		Recommended stocking and spacing after thinning or releasing for different product objectives[2]			
			Veneer logs		Veneer logs and nuts	
	Trees per acre	Spacing between trees	Trees per acre	Spacing between trees	Trees per acre	Spacing between trees
	Number	Feet	Number	Feet	Number	Feet
2	797	7	265	13	225	14
4	380	11	175	16	150	17
6	223	14	125	19	105	20
8	147	17	90	22	80	23
10	104	20	70	25	60	27
12	78	24	55	28	50	30
14	60	27	45	31	40	33
16	48	30	40	33	35	35
18	39	33	35	35	30	38
20	32	37	30	38	25	42
22	27	40	--	--	--	--
24	23	43	--	--	--	--

[1] Obtained by using the following equation (Krajicek 1966): crown width in feet = 1.993 d.b.h. in inches + 4.873.

[2] These values are based on the assumption that crop trees will grow 4 inches in diameter before they again need to be thinned or released.

Table 2. — *Effect of crown release on 5-year growth of individual walnut trees in seven stands on a wide range of site conditions*

Stand No.	Site condition	Average age	Crown release treatment	No. of trees	Initial d.b.h.	Initial crown area	5-year growth D.b.h	5-year growth Crown area
		Years			Inches	Square feet	Inches	Square feet
1	Moderately deep silty alluvium over coarse chert deposits	25	Not released Released	12 32	5.59 5.86	86 110	0.25 .52	-3 22
2	Ungraded, strip-mine spoil material	28	Not released Released	5 41	6.59 5.71	107 103	.62 .79	18 41
3	Ungraded, strip-mine spoil material	28	Not released Released	12 40	6.35 6.92	118 166	.63 1.22	36 116
4	Imperfectly drained flood-plain soils	25	Not released Released	13 64	7.22 7.47	151 159	1.21 1.32	23 86
5	Imperfectly to well-drained floodplain soils	25	Not released Released	27 67	8.70 8.03	203 192	.98 1.24	39 88
6	Well-drained upland sandy till soils	40-60+	Not released Released	11 25	12.93 13.93	303 346	.76 .97	14 142
7	Imperfectly drained, lower slope	40-60+	Not released Released	15 29	13.28 13.30	363 406	.85 .94	165 212

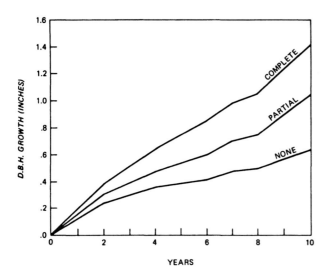

Figure 2. — *Complete crown release stimulated the diameter growth of these pole-sized walnut trees for at least 8 years; a second light release after 8 years further improved growth.*

ana, for example, did not result in any significant growth responses over a 5-year period. Complete understory vegetation control required frequent retreatment (almost annually), which was time-consuming and costly. Therefore, unless the understory vegetation is extremely dense, control is probably not justified on good sites. On poorer sites, where moisture stress is more severe or where nut production is a major product objective, control of understory vegetation may be more beneficial (Holt and Voeller 1971).

Release and thinning of sawtimber-sized trees do not appear to result in much growth improvement. Clark (1967) reported that small sawtimber-sized trees averaging 13 inches in diameter responded less to complete crown release than pole-sized trees averaging only 9 inches in diameter. Nor did the small sawtimber-sized trees in Illinois and Indiana (stands 6 and 7) show much response to crown release (table 2). Apparently the potential for crown expansion is limited on larger trees, and any growth stimulation from release is small and distributed over a larger bole volume. Thinning can probably be justified in these older stands, however, on the basis of improving nut production. These nuts can be collected and sold, or left to help establish a new stand by natural regeneration. Intermediate thinnings in older stands also make it possible to salvage weaker but merchantable trees that might not survive until final harvest.

PRUNE TO IMPROVE QUALITY

Selected crop trees should be pruned early in the rotation for the greatest improvement in form and quality. Many of the crooks and forks commonly found in established sapling stands could have been avoided had the seedlings been correctively pruned. Corrective pruning can begin when trees are only 2 to 3 years old, and should continue until a straight, branch-free log 9 feet or longer has been produced (Krajicek and Bey 1969). The more misshapen seedlings should be coppiced in early spring (before June 1) and the new sprouts thinned and tended as new trees. Most naturally established seedlings and saplings also frequently need to be correctively pruned or coppiced to improve their form and growth.

Clear-length pruning can be started when the trees are only sapling size, but it is better to wait until the trees are 3 to 6 inches d.b.h. (fig. 3). Pruning too many branches from the main crown of small trees frequently reduces diameter growth and causes top-heavy crowns, which may break off during strong winds. Clear-length pruning will generally be needed sooner in open stands and widely spaced plantings than in crowded stands where natural pruning has removed many of the lower limbs. By the time a tree is 8 to 10 inches d.b.h. it is marginal for pruning because there will not be enough clear wood produced over the pruning wounds to greatly increase log value when the tree is harvested.

Branches should be cut off nearly flush with the main tree bole, but cutting deep into the branch collar should be avoided. The deeper the cut is made into the branch collar the larger the pruning wound. The pruned branch stub should not exceed ½ inch in length. The best time to prune is during the late dormant season, and the worst time is midsummer to late summer. The tissue around summer-pruned branch stubs may die back, causing an enlarged pruning wound and slower healing.

It is recommended that no more than a third of the live crown be removed at any one time, even though past research has shown that up to half of the live crown

Figure 3. — *Releasing and pruning immature walnut trees will improve the growth and form and increase their potential value when finally harvested. No more than one-third of the crown should be removed in pruning, and the total live crown ratio should never be reduced to less than half the total tree height. Removing all vines from these trees will help maintain good growth and form.*

can be pruned without reducing growth (Clark and Seidel 1961). Frequent light prunings are recommended over heavy prunings because there is less risk of over-pruning. All pruning should be restricted to the lower half of the bole. How high to prune depends on the product objective and on the cost and difficulty of pruning. When nut production is a major goal, a fairly large crown is needed. Thus on these trees, pruning should be limited to the butt log. The minimum length to prune is 9 feet, but when veneer-log production is a major goal, it may be profitable to prune as high as 25 feet. Pruning above 25 feet is very difficult and expensive.

Some followup pruning may be needed to remove sprouts that have developed around the pruning wounds. These sprouts should be removed as soon as possible to prevent the formation of knots. Epicormic sprouting

53

is sometimes stimulated by releasing the trees, but it is not recommended that pruning be delayed if the trees are to be released. The sooner the branches are pruned the sooner they will heal over and the more clear wood that will be produced. An extensive release-pruning study in progress shows that if the sprouts on released trees are pruned off a few times, the frequency of re-sprouting can be greatly reduced.

FERTILIZATION

Fertilizer may be needed on certain sites to obtain maximum yields. Research and experience have demonstrated that pole-sized and larger walnut trees on the less fertile upland sites are most responsive to supplemental fertilization. Fertilizing seedlings and small saplings is not recommended because it only stimulates weed growth and complicates weed control. The older trees seem most responsive to nitrogen fertilization. In one walnut stand in southern Wisconsin, for example, pelleted ammonium nitrate was applied at the rate of 500 pounds of nitrogen per acre around 10 of 20 paired trees on a bottomland site and around 10 of 20 paired trees on an upland site (Anonymous 1968). The trees ranged from 8 to 14 inches d.b.h. and up to 70 feet tall. After 2 years the fertilized trees on the upland site were growing 34 percent faster in diameter than the unfertilized trees. After 4 years the trees were refertilized, and by the end of the seventh growing season, cumulative diameter growth on the upland site was still 37 percent greater for fertilized trees than for unfertilized trees.[2] On the bottomland soils the trees showed little or no response to fertilization, even after reapplication, probably because the soils were already quite fertile.

Much additional research must be completed before fertilization can become a practical management tool for walnut growers. Needed are better methods for diagnosing specific nutrient deficiencies and better infor-

mation on where, when how much, and how often to fertilize for greatest responses. Some tentative guidelines for diagnosing nutrient deficiencies by analyzing the foliage of walnut trees have been proposed (Phares and Finn 1972), but such procedures need more field testing. Even though nitrogen deficiencies are most frequently encountered, elements such as potassium are also needed in larger quantities, especially for nut production, and may be deficient on more sites than commonly thought (Shear 1971). Other specific nutrient needs will undoubtedly be discovered with further research. At least in the foreseeable future walnut growers should concentrate management on the more fertile sites and fertilize only on an experimental basis. Before fertilization is even considered, growers should first make sure the crop trees have been adequately released, thinned, and pruned.

LITERATURE CITED

Anonymous. 1968. Walnut responds well to treatment in FPL research. For. Ind. 95(2): 34-35, illus.

Clark, F. Bryan. 1967. Pole-sized black walnut responds quickly to crown release. J. For. 65(6): 406-408, illus.

Clark, F. Bryan, and Kenneth W. Seidel. 1961. Growth and quality of pruned black walnut (*Juglans nigra*). USDA For. Serv. Tech. Pap. 180, 11 p., illus.

Geyer, W. A., and G. G. Naughton. 1971. Growth and management of black walnut (*Juglans nigra* L.) on strip-mined lands in southeastern Kansas. Kans. Acad. Sci. Trans. 73(4): 491-501, illus.

Holt, H. A., and J. E. Voeller. 1971. Effect of vegetation control on established black walnuts. Arkansas Farm Res. 21(1): 8.

Krajicek, John E. 1966. Growing space requirements. *In* Black walnut culture, p. 47-49, illus. USDA For. Serv., North Cent. For. Exp. Stn., St. Paul, Minn.

Krajicek, John E., and Calvin F. Bey. 1969. How to "train" black walnut seedlings. USDA For. Serv., North Cent. For. Exp. Stn., St. Paul, Minn. 5 p., illus.

Phares, Robert E., and Raymond F. Finn. 1972. Using foliage analysis to help diagnose nutrient deficiencies in black walnut. North. Nut Grow. Assoc. Annu. Rep. 62(1971): 98-104, illus.

Phares, Robert E., and Robert D. Williams. 1971. Crown release promotes faster diameter growth of pole-size black walnut. USDA For. Serv. Res. Note NC-124, 4 p., illus. North Cent. For. Exp. Stn., St. Paul, Minn.

Shear, C. B. 1971. Importance of potassium in the nutrition of nut trees. North. Nut Grow. Assoc. Annu. Rep. 61(1970): 25-28.

---

[2] *Personal communication with Robert R. Maeglin, Forest Products Laboratory, Madison, Wisconsin. December 5, 1972.*

TREE CULTURE IN THE SOUTHEAST

Warren Giles Boyette, *Project Forester*
North Carolina Forest Service
Morganton, North Carolina

ABSTRACT.—Black walnut is scarce in hardwood stands of the Southeast but good potential exists for growing more quality timber. Recent silvicultural knowledge coupled with research findings in other regions make the growing of black walnut practical. Problems, research results, and current recommendations are given for seed collection, nursery practices, site selection and preparation, plantings and cultural practices. Silvicultural goals are stated and the problems needing further research are defined.

The Southeast has a widely recognized reputation as one of the most productive hardwood timber growing regions in the United States. The favorable climate and good soils contribute to sites suitable for more commercial hardwood species than any other region in the United States. Black walnut is one of these species, growing naturally on the best sites from the lower coastal plain to the higher mountains.

During the past century most of the hardwood stands in the Southeast have been cut over at least twice. High-grading has effectively removed the better timber and left the poorer timber as growing stock.

Because of its high value, black walnut has been especially vulnerable to high-grading with the result that it has now become scarce. Most of the black walnut now exists as single trees along stream banks, in pastures and mountain coves, or near old farm buildings. Usually these remaining trees are short-boled, heavy-limbed, and have little commercial value (Brenneman 1971).

The Southeast is not usually considered a region with a high potential for growing significant quantities of quality black walnut timber, but several factors favor growing more black walnut. Because of the numerous deep and well-drained stream bottoms in all physiographic regions, and the deep, fertile coves in the mountains, black walnut occurs from elevations of near sea level to 3,500 feet. Although each site is usually small in acreage, the sites are numerous. Because of the high rainfall, warm temperatures, and long growing season, rotations are short. The wood furniture industry is centered in North Carolina, giving the Southeast an established home market.

Recent studies indicate that the machining properties of fast-growing black walnut are equal or superior to slow-growing trees. Also, the darker heartwood color is advantageous (Englerth 1966), and the sapwood can be treated to closely approach the color of natural heartwood (Brauner and Loos 1968). These findings tend to refute a frequent argument used to discriminate against the fast-growing black walnut typical of the Southeast — that it is unsuitable for veneer.

To date, no appreciable acreage has been planted to black walnut. The reasons for this are a lack of silvicultural knowledge about growing black walnut, and the fact that most of the past plantings have been failures. These two factors have kept many foresters from promoting the planting of black walnut in the Southeast.

Only in the last 5 years has marked emphasis been put on acquiring the silvicultural knowledge required to plant and grow black walnut. Two State forestry agencies, the North Carolina Forest Service and the Virginia Division of Forestry, have experimental programs emphasizing black walnut silviculture. Experimentation has necessarily included seed collection, nursery practices, planting, and plantation cultural practices. By combining these results with the results of research efforts elsewhere, primarily in the Midwest, considerably more is now known about the silviculture of growing black walnut in the Southeast than was known 5 years ago.

SEED COLLECTION

For nursery production most black walnut seed are now collected without regard to source. Recent publications indicate that seed source may be important in black walnut (Bey *et al.* 1971, Wright and Lemmien 1972). Bey (1972) reported that seed from southern sources produce trees whose leaves flush earlier and drop earlier, grow taller, and have more lateral buds on the current year's terminal than trees from northern sources. Deneke and Funsch (1970) found survival higher after two growing seasons for southeastern sources than local Kansas sources.

Because of the range in elevation within the Southeastern Region, it is suspected that growth patterns differ significantly among physiographic provinces. The State forestry agencies of North Carolina and Virginia have separate geographic seed source studies underway to determine if seed collection should be segregated by physiographic provinces; i.e., the mountains, piedmont, and coastal plain. The study in Virginia has seed sources from elevations of 500 to 2,000 feet; the one in North Carolina from elevations of less than 100 up to 3,500 feet. Answers should be available in 3 to 5 years.

NURSERY PRACTICES

Seedling size, provided the seedling has an adequate root system, is perhaps one of the most reliable indicators of growth potential when the seedling is outplanted. Most studies to date indicate the larger the seedling diameter at root collar, the better the height growth. The maximum feasible root collar diameter has not yet been determined; the economics of producing the seedling in the nursery will certainly be one limiting factor. A minimum root collar diameter of one-half to three-fourths of an inch has been suggested by the hardwood silviculture foresters of the North Carolina Forest Service.

Essential for the growing of large seedlings is an abundance of water, proper fertilization, and proper seedbed density. It is doubtful that current fertilization regimes are the best and more work is required in this area. To attain the desired seedling, a density of no more than five per square foot is recommended.

When seedlings are lifted, care must be taken to ensure that as much of the root system as possible is left intact. Large diameter seedlings need large fibrous root systems to support the shoot.

PLANTING CONSIDERATIONS

Methods

Seedling planting has been far more successful than the planting of nuts. By planting the proper size seedling, at least 2 years' growth is gained. Rodent damage and vegetative competition are also reduced.

The planting of potted black walnut by the North Carolina Forest Service during the summer months has been successful. Planting 2- to 3-month-old seedlings in 5-inch diameter by 7-inch-high peat pots resulted in survival averages over 90 percent, except where the peat pots were not placed below the soil surface. If left exposed, the pots act as a wick by absorbing soil moisture from the root zone and transpiring the moisture into the atmosphere. The planting season could be extended into the summer months with the use of potted seedlings.

Large, bare-rooted seedlings must be carefully planted. The shovel is the best planting tool for large root systems, but the posthole digger, mattock, and power auger are also good. The power auger is fastest, but if the holes are made too deep a depression occurs from soil settling after planting that may allow standing water.

To allow for soil settling, the seedling should be planted deep enough so that the root collar is 1 to 2 inches beneath the soil surface.

Association Plantings

European black alder and black locust are currently being alternately planted with black walnut. Both species are known to increase the available nitrogen thereby increasing black walnut growth. Presently, European black alder is favored because of its exceptional growth, and the prospect that the trees can eventually be sold as pulpwood for additional income. No known association plantings are old enough to determine whether detrimental effects may occur, such as overtopping of the black walnut by the nurse species.

SITE SELECTION AND PREPARATION

No silvicultural practice can rescue a black walnut plantation on an unsuitable site. Desirable sites in the Southeast are deep, fertile, well-drained, loamy soils usually found in the small stream bottoms and terraces, and the mountain coves. Moisture is probably the most critical site factor. Too much or too little moisture is devastating, but no definite upper or lower limits have been determined. Black walnut can tolerate some flooding, provided the water leaves in a few hours. One successful planting was flooded four times the first year and at least twice annually the next 3 years. Water never remained more than 24 hours except in a small area where the trees died. Such a difference in microsite is easily overlooked, but is extremely important.

The planting area should be free of competition. Plowing, disking, hand tools, and chemicals are satisfactory means of controlling competition. However, the best growth achieved by the North Carolina Forest Service has been on "bedded" sites.

Bedded sites are planting beds raised 10 to 15 inches in height and measuring 3 to 5 feet in width. Beds are formed with standard bedding plows, large roto tillers, or farm plows. Bedding creates a planting medium with better soil aeration and better soil water percolation in the feeder root zone. The major advantage is decreased weed competition in the first year after planting. Before planting, the beds must be allowed to settle preferably for several months; at least two heavy rains are also required. So impressive have been the results, that bedding is now recommended for all black walnut plantings in North Carolina.

CULTURAL PRACTICES

Weed Control

Woody vegetation, grasses, and vines compete most severely with black walnut; herbaceous plants compete very little and their effect on growth is negligible.

Hand tools have been used for weed control with success but chemicals are better, less expensive, and easier (see page 114). A pamphlet, *Weed Control in Black Walnut Plantings* (Krajicek 1969), is suggested for more complete information.

Fertilization

Better knowledge of the soil nutrient requirements for optimum growth of black walnut is needed. Serious nutrient imbalance, however, can be detected by chemical analysis. Thus, representative soil samples should be taken on a prospective planting site. A fertilizer, chosen on the basis of the analysis, should be applied before or at the time of site preparation to bring the site up to suggested nutrient levels.

After planting, fertilization is generally not recommended in the early years nor at the time of coppicing because it can stimulate undesirable growth in the seedling and increase competition from weeds. Overstimulation from fertilizer has resulted in heavy top growth and succulent stems subject to breakage from wind or their own weight. The one case in which fertilizer is applied to young trees to stimulate growth is when a young plantation has not started growing after 2 years in the field.

Side Pruning

The side pruning studies in the Southeast are for the most part less than 4 years old. No side pruning should be done until after the third growing season, perhaps longer. Large limbs that will not callus over quickly should not be pruned. Clark (1971) suggests that no limb over 1 inch in diameter should be pruned. Pruning has been done as late as April in North Carolina without any apparent detrimental effects; thus, side pruning anytime during the dormant season is considered satisfactory. To maintain tree balance, no more than one-half the length of the tree should be without side limbs.

Corrective Pruning and Coppicing

The high incidence of dieback is the most frustrating silvicultural problem in growing black walnut. Multiple stem tops are a common occurrence, especially in the early years. When a tree with a poorly formed top has less than the minimal 9 feet of potentially straight stem, either corrective pruning or coppicing is required.

Corrective pruning is recommended only to release a leader which will maintain an acceptable stem thereafter. Results show that if corrective pruning must be applied to a tree for more than 1 year, stem crook often becomes too great to achieve a desirable stem. If this occurs, no choice exists but to coppice.

Coppicing is the best way to correct poorly formed trees with less than 9 feet of acceptable stem. Tests in both natural and planted black walnut indicate that coppicing can be done anytime during the dormant season. Stems should be cut at an angle less than 2 inches from the ground. Once a 9-foot high acceptable stem is attained, coppicing should not be considered.

Multiple stems usually occur after coppicing. Present recommendations are to select the most vigorous, straight sprout in the early spring following coppicing. Other sprouts should be removed immediately to encourage more growth on the selected sprout.

ACCEPTABLE GROWTH AND SILVICULTURAL GOALS

Most black walnut seedlings grow very little the first year after planting, but should accelerate in growth the second year. Although growth will vary widely by sites, by the fourth year it should exceed a foot per year. Anything less indicates that something is wrong—improper site, poor seedlings, poor site preparation, inadequate weed control. Growth in black walnut plantings in the Southeast has varied from poor to excellent. Poor growth can usually be traced to not following a recommended practice. Best growth in a young plantation averages 15 feet after 4 years. To achieve the desired rotation age of 35 to 40 years for veneer logs, early growth is essential.

Seventeen feet of acceptable stem in the butt cut of the tree is the current goal of black walnut silviculture. However, the mills in the Southeast will process logs with as little as 9 feet of acceptable stem in the butt cut.

NEEDED RESEARCH

Considerable progress is being made toward making the growing of black walnut in the Southeast more profitable, but problems do exist which hinder our program. Continued and new research are needed on:

(a) Geographic variability of seed source in the Southeast.

(b) Upper and lower limits of nursery seedling water requirements.

(c) Proper fertilizer regimes in the nursery.

(d) Causes of and the regulation of the high incidence of dieback in young trees.

(e) Fertilization of young plantations.

(f) Acceptability of fast-growing black walnut for lumber and veneer.

(g) Improving logging and milling technology so that short logs can be utilized.

SUMMARY

The Southeast presently has no appreciable volume of quality black walnut sawtimber or veneer timber because of the repeated high-grading of the timber stands in the past. Suitable sites do exist, however, from the coastal plain to the mountains. The furniture industry of the United States is centered in the Southeast and is a readily available market for quality wood. Only recently has the planting of black walnut and the required silvicultural practices been examined in detail. Midwestern growers have made black walnut culture successful and practical through research. Continued experimentation, careful promotion, and the use of known silvicultural methods can achieve the same results in the Southeast. The present goal is to grow a 17-foot butt log suitable for veneer within 35 or 40 years. Problems needing new and continued research are listed.

LITERATURE CITED

Bey, Calvin F. 1972. Trends in growth of black walnut originating in various geographic areas. North. Nut Grow. Assoc. Annu. Rep. 62 (1971): 83-86, illus.

Bey, Calvin F., John R. Toliver, and Paul L. Roth. 1971. Early growth of black walnut trees from twenty seed sources. USDA For. Serv. Res. Note NC-105, 4 p. North Cent. For. Exp. Stn., St. Paul, Minn.

Brauner, A. B., and W. E. Loos. 1968. Color changes in black walnut (Juglans nigra) as a function of temperature, time, and two moisture conditions. For. Prod. J. 18(5): 29-34.

Brenneman, Dwight L. 1971. Growing black walnut in North Carolina. South. Lumberman 223(2776): 165-167.

Clark, F. Bryan. 1971. Planting black walnut for timber. USDA For. Serv. Leafl. 487 (Rev.), 10 p., illus.

Deneke, F. J., and R. W. Funsch. 1970. Early notes on black walnut provenance tests in Kansas. Kan. Acad. Sci. Trans. 72(3): 404-405.

Englerth, George H. 1966. Machining and other properties of fast- versus slow-grown trees. In Black walnut culture. USDA For. Serv., p. 77-82, illus. North Cent. For. Exp. Stn., St. Paul, Minn.

Krajicek, John E. 1969. Weed control in black walnut plantings. North. Nut Grow. Assoc. Annu. Rep. 60: 30-35, illus.

Wright, Jonathan W., and Walter A. Lemmien. 1972. Seven-year results from black walnut and black cherry provenance tests in Michigan. Eighth Cent. States For. Tree Improv. Conf., Columbia, Mo. 10 p.

GENETICS AND TREE IMPROVEMENT

David T. Funk, *Principal Plant Geneticist*
Forestry Sciences Laboratory, North Central Forest Experiment Station
Carbondale, Illinois[1]

ABSTRACT.—Recent progress of walnut genetic research and action programs has been good. It is possible to make considerable genetic gains for growth traits simply by using walnut planting stock of appropriate geographic origin. The prospects for vegetative propagation are now considerably improved, for rooting of cuttings as well as grafting.

Just as with any other crop, the genetic improvement of black walnut consists of determining the extent of heritable variation, identifying and selecting individual plants possessing desirable genetic traits, and interbreeding these trees to produce certified seed. Walnut tree improvement is making steady progress along this course.

The history of black walnut genetics and tree improvement is not really crowded with heroes. Aside from pioneering hybridization by Burbank, and the evidence of racial variation demonstrated by Emerson (1906) and Wright (1954), nearly all early efforts were directed toward selection, breeding, and propagation of improved nut varieties. Until the time of the Walnut Workshop 7 years ago, work on genetic improvement of black walnut for timber production lacked both volume and continuity (Wright 1966). I am pleased to report a considerable upsurge in the volume of walnut genetic research and action programs; if we can maintain the necessary continuity, the prospects for real progress are good.

PROGRESS

Over the past 12 years, Forest Service research by F. Bryan Clark, myself, and especially by Calvin Bey has confirmed the importance of racial genetic variation in several important characteristics of black walnut (Bey 1973). For most traits of phenology and growth in young plantations, differences among seed sources were considerably larger than differences among trees within stands or stands within areas (Bey 1970; Bey, Hawker, and Roth 1971). The significance of these findings is

that it is possible to make considerable genetic gains simply by using walnut planting stock of appropriate geographic origin; all of our tests to date indicate that seed should be collected from south of the intended planting site.

McKay (1966) characterized vegetative propagation of black walnut as either "unsuccessful" or "unreliable," but the situation is no longer so bleak. Attempts to root cuttings were indeed generally unsuccessful in the past, but Shreve and Miles (1972) have reported striking success in rooting black walnut cuttings originating from adventitious buds. More important, the technique that they used worked as well with mature trees as with seedlings.

Walnut grafting is no longer as unreliable as before. Over a 4-year span, Masters and Beineke (1973) achieved 81 to 100 percent success for three methods of grafting in the greenhouse and growth chamber. In the field, the success rate for inlay grafting, the best method tested, ranged from 33 to 83 percent. I believe that black walnut continues to earn the distinction of being "perhaps more difficult than any other hardwood species" to propagate (McKay 1966), but we no longer need to be resigned to failure; the job can be done.

Progress in controlled breeding of walnut has been slow and probably will continue to be so. Since walnut flowers usually occur singly or in clusters of two or three, their isolation and pollination is much less efficient than for such species as pines or yellow-poplar in which seed is borne in cones. The techniques of controlled pollination carried out most extensively by Tucovic in Yugoslavia are not unusual, but seed set is often very low. Some progress has been made in im-

[1] *Laboratory maintained in cooperation with Southern Illinois University.*

proving methods for long-term storage of pollen to allow making otherwise impossible crosses. We can now systematically verify the hybridity of walnut seedlings of some of the common species combinations. But at least for the near future, most of our breeding work will be based on open-pollinated seed.

Over the past few years, several State forestry agencies and the National Forest System have taken steps to maintain better control over the sources of their walnut seed supply. At least four States and National Forests have developed seed production areas that are bearing on a regular basis. And nine States and National Forests have established seed orchards that will add an important contribution to the walnut seed supply when they come into full production. Many nurserymen have divided their States into regions and ship walnut planting stock to tree planters for use in the same area in which the seed was collected. Industrial cooperators are also working to ensure that the seed they provide to the States is kept separate by collection zones and distributed to appropriate nurseries.

A less tangible component of progress in walnut genetics is cooperation. University, industrial, State, and Federal tree improvement workers have formed an unusually close network to expedite seed collection and exchange, planting stock production, experimental plantation establishment and maintenance, data collection, and sharing of results and recommendations. To cite an example from our program at Carbondale, in addition to field studies located on our own experimental areas using our own personnel, we depended on cooperators to help establish at least 42 separate walnut research plantings in 15 States. Most of these plantations are thriving, being actively managed, and yielding increasingly useful information. Intensive and enthusiastic cooperation has been absolutely essential to get the job done.

WHAT NEXT?

Understandably enough, selection in most walnut genetic improvement programs has been directed toward climatic adaptation, increased growth rate, and improved tree form. We have a long chore ahead of us before achieving maximum progress with these objectives, and now is certainly no time to relax the effort. But I suggest that as we begin to make some genetic progress toward these original goals, we should broaden our effort to include improved seed production and pest resistance. From the forest tree improvement standpoint increased seed producing capability has obvious benefits to seed

orchard managers; I believe that this trait will be even more valuable in terms of breeding dual-purpose trees for production of both nuts and timber. Inherently pest-resistant trees are obviously desirable and there is no doubt that insect and disease problems seem to be greater in intensively cultured plantations than in natural stands. These difficulties are likely to be compounded as we are faced with increasingly stringent restrictions on use of pesticides; the search for genetic pest resistance may provide the *only* acceptable solution.

Tree improvement and tree planting must and should be tightly linked. A large tree planting program justifies a comparable tree improvement effort because the genetically improved planting stock can be used on a broad scale. Conversely, seed and seedlings of the highest genetic quality are of little value if they are not used in reforestation, either because their superior worth is not recognized or simply because there is generally little demand for the species. Such is certainly not the situation with black walnut. The demand for planting stock has quadrupled over the past 10 years to total more than three million seedlings and stratified nuts shipped by State nurseries each year (Williams and Phares 1973).

The opportunity is at hand to plant improved walnut trees on a broad scale. But tree planters are not receiving the genetically superior planting stock that they need. Why is this so? I believe that there are at least two underlying problems and perhaps three solutions to them. The first problem is the scarcity of improved seed, and in some years, a general shortage of walnuts over large portions of the range. A short-term solution to this problem is to improve methods of seed storage so that good crops can be held over until later years; this sort of information should be available in the near future. A long-term solution to the problem lies in one of our specific objectives: creation of orchards with sufficient capacity to supply the needed seed.

Another problem related to the shortage of genetically improved walnut planting stock is that we are simply not doing the best job we know how to do. I mentioned in complimentary terms the development of seed production areas and seed orchards, establishment of seed collection zones and other real progress that has been made in the past few years. But the fact is that much of the walnut planting stock shipped today is of unknown or unsuitable geographic origin. We all know the reasons, "We ran out of seed and had to buy from Siberia," or "I know that we should collect seed from that area, but we aren't allowed to cross the river." Nevertheless, the tree planter who receives seedlings or seed of improper origin has to live with *our mistakes* for the life of his plantation. It's time to shape up.

LITERATURE CITED

Bey, Calvin F. 1970. Geographic variation for seed and seedling characters in black walnut. USDA For. Serv. Res. Note NC-101, 4 p., illus. North Cent. For. Exp. Stn., St. Paul, Minn.

Bey, Calvin F. 1973. Growth of black walnut trees in eight midwestern States — a provenance test. USDA For. Serv. Res. Note. North Cent. For. Exp. Stn., St. Paul, Minn. (In press.)

Bey, Calvin F., Norman L. Hawker, and Paul L. Roth. 1971. Variations in growth and form in young plantation black walnut trees. South. For. Tree Improv. Conf. Proc. 11: 120-127, illus.

Emerson, R. A. 1906. The relation of early maturity to hardiness in trees. Nebr. Agric. Exp. Stn. Annu. Rep. 19: 101-110, illus.

McKay, J. W. 1966. Vegetative propagation. *In* Black walnut culture. p. 58-61. USDA For. Serv., North Cent. For. Exp. Stn., St. Paul, Minn.

Masters, Charles J. and Walter F. Beineke. 1973. Clonal vs. half-sib seedling orchards for black walnut. Northeast. For. Tree Improv. Conf. Proc. 20. (In press.)

Shreve, Loy W., and Neil W. Miles. 1972. Propagating black walnut clones from rooted cuttings. Plant Propagator 18(3): 4-7.

Williams, Robert D., and Robert E. Phares. 1973. Black walnut seedling production and related nursery research. Northeast. Area Nurserymen's Conf. Proc. (In press.)

Wright, J. W. 1954. Preliminary report on a study of races in black walnut. J. For. 52: 673-675.

Wright, J. W. 1966. Breeding better timber varieties. *In* Black walnut culture. p. 53-57. USDA For. Serv., North Cent. For. Exp. Stn., St. Paul, Minn.

GENETIC VARIATION AND SELECTION

Calvin F. Bey, *Plant Geneticist*
Forestry Sciences Laboratory, North Central Forest Experiment Station
Carbondale, Illinois[1]

ABSTRACT.—Research dealing with genetic variation and selection in black walnut has confirmed the idea of wide genetic diversity. Growth, form, leaf flush, leaf fall, and period of growth are genetically variable. Leaf flush usually begins 1 day earlier for every 85 miles south of the planting site that seed is collected. In field tests, leaf fall is delayed about 1 day for every 25 miles to the south that seed is collected. Trees from as far as 200 miles south of the planting site generally grow as large or larger in height and diameter than trees from local or northern sources.

Where variation exists, we have a choice. We don't have to be satisfied with brand X; we select the brand that pleases us most. The same thing is true in tree improvement. We compare trees of various origins with some standard (brand X) and then select the trees that please us most. For a given character, the amount of improvement possible depends largely on the degree of genetic variation present, or on how superior the selected tree is compared with a standard.

Fragments of genetic information available before 1966 suggested that there were good possibilities for genetic improvement of black walnut. Reports of trees growing in plantations north of their natural range suggested that there was inherent variation in cold hardiness. The many named nut varieties of black walnut showed that variation was present in nut and kernel characteristics. Coupled with this evidence of variation, we knew that walnut grew on diverse sites, over a wide range of climatic conditions, and that it was primarily an outcrossing species. There was reason to begin research and improvement programs on an optimistic note.

During the past 7 years, research and action programs have confirmed the idea of wide genetic diversity. Growth, form, leaf flush, leaf fall, and period of growth are some characters that are genetically variable. Nursery results in a range-wide seed source study showed that for most characters studied there was a gradual increase or decrease from north to south. Results from outplantings at many locations have supported this variation pattern.

---

[1] *The Station's laboratory in Carbondale is maintained in cooperation with Southern Illinois University.*

The relative importance of geographic variation (among stands) and local variation (within stands) has been studied. Evidence is clear that geographic variation is several times greater than local variation for most characters. The importance of using the proper geographic source of seed cannot be emphasized enough. On the other hand, local genetic variation is large enough so that it should not be ignored in improvement programs. In other words, within a designated seed collection zone, there is additional opportunity to make genetic gain through selection.

CHARACTER VARIATION

Seed Size

There is a wide range in seed size but no geographic area produces unusually large or small seed. Average fresh weight of seed from 456 individual trees representing 69 geographic sources was 22 grams. Average seed weight varied from 5 to 40 grams for individual trees and from 12 to 30 grams for sources. The average seed weight for individual trees within the same source differed by 10 grams or more in more than half of the sources. Much additional work has been done on nut traits, but it is not included here as we are dealing primarily with timber traits.

Survival

In 6-year-old provenance tests in Illinois, Missouri, Indiana, Kansas, Iowa, and Michigan, survival was *not* related to the latitude of the sources. The sources included in these tests were generally from 200 miles north to 400 miles south of the planting site. In an Ohio provenance test, survival after 6 years was generally higher for the southern sources. The trend was weak, however; only 30 percent of the variation associated with survival was accounted for by the latitude of seed source. In a 6-year-old Minnesota test, there was a strong continuous trend with latitude, with higher survival in trees from northern sources (all sources were from south of the planting site). Seventy-six percent of the trees from 250 miles south of the planting site survived, while only 29 percent of the trees from 250 to 650 miles south survived. Seventy-nine percent of the variation associated with survival was accounted for by the latitude of seed source.

Leaf Flush

Trees that break dormancy early are more susceptible to spring frost damage than late-flushing trees. The time of black walnut leaf expansion in the spring has been studied in five plantations located in Michigan, Ohio, and Illinois. Flushing was recorded in 1969, 1970, and 1971 in one Illinois plantation and in 1971 in the other four plantations. Leaf flush is considered to have occurred when the first leaf on the tree is 1 inch long.

In all plantations trees from the southern sources flushed earlier than trees from northern sources. On the average, flushing began 1 day earlier for every 85 miles south of the planting site that seed was collected.

As would be expected, trees in northern plantations generally flush later than trees in southern plantations. In plantations in Michigan, Ohio, and Illinois, flushing in 1971 was delayed about 4 days for every 100 miles to the north that the plantation was located. However, local and microclimatic environmental conditions can influence the date of leaf flush. For instance, on two southern Illinois sites about 15 miles apart, trees on an upland site flushed about 4 days earlier than those on a bottomland site. Apparently the soil was drier on the exposed upland site, allowing the soil to warm up sooner than on the bottomland site. Trees from the same families flushed first on both the upland and the bottomland site.

In one plantation in Illinois the average flushing date differed by only 3 days over 3 years of tallying, ranging from April 25 to April 28. Trees that flushed early one year also flushed early the next.

Heritability (the degree to which a character is influenced by heredity as compared with environment) for date of leaf flush was 0.67 and 0.96 in two separate 2-year-old 85-family progeny tests and 0.67 in a 4-year-old 17-family test. Although these high heritabilities indicate that the chances for making genetic gains for this character are good, even with intensive selection it appears that within any seed collection zone we would not be able to delay flushing more than a few days.

Leaf Fall

In three separate tests, leaf fall showed strong trends with latitude. Trees from southern sources drop their leaves later than trees from northern sources. This information has been known since 1906 when Emerson conducted a test with walnut in Nebraska. In a recent nursery test, leaf fall was delayed about 1 day for every 200 miles south of the nursery that seed was collected. In two field tests, the delay was about 1 day for every 25 miles. Early autumn watering in the nursery usually causes the leaves to hang on longer than normal; leaf fall in the nursery then generally occurs in a relatively short time. In the three tests mentioned, latitude of seed source accounted for 74, 77, and 96 percent of the variation associated with date of leaf fall. In a plantation of 4-year-old trees in southern Illinois, leaf fall in trees from the southernmost sources (Texas and Mississippi) did not occur until after the first hard freeze in 1969. We speculated that trees holding their leaves until late fall might not be winter-hardy. But there was no evidence of winter dieback, so the buds and stems were apparently mature and well hardened. The period between height-growth cessation and leaf fall was about 11 weeks for all trees.

Height and Diameter

At eight locations (mentioned in section on survival) trees from as far as 200 miles south of the planting site generally grew as large or larger in height and diameter than trees from local or northern sources. Although in Missouri, Illinois, Indiana, and Michigan, sources from more than 200 miles south generally were larger than local sources, we would not recommend going beyond 200 miles south of the planting zone for seed collection for reforestation purposes. In an Iowa and Minnesota provenance test, we found a definite limit on how far northward walnut seed can be safely moved without reducing growth. Trees from sources more than 200 miles south of the planting site generally were smaller than local sources.

Duration of growth and rate of growth are both responsible for some of the growth differences. In 1969 in one southern Illinois plantation, trees from Mississippi and Texas grew in height for 134 days, compared with 93 days for trees from northern Illinois and Iowa. On the average, height growth continued 1 day longer for every 24 miles south of the planting site that seed was collected. Most height growth takes place in a short time. In 1967 and 1968 in southern Illinois, 90 percent of the height growth for the year was completed in 8 to 10 weeks.

Duration of diameter growth is less closely related to latitude of origin than is duration of height growth. One study of 4-year-old trees showed no correlation between latitude of origin and number of days of diameter growth, or between latitude and the date by which 90 percent of the diameter growth occurred. However, trees of southern origin grew faster than those from the north. Differences among the groups gradually increased throughout the growing season.

In a pot study with 1-year-old trees, we found that shoot and root dry weight differences among sources generally increased with time. Although height growth was complete by mid-July, shoot dry weight increased until mid-August and root dry weight increased until mid-September or time of leaf fall.

The importance of geographic variation has also been demonstrated in an 85-family combination progeny test-seedling seed orchard in southern Illinois. The collection zone for the test included an area from 150 miles to the north to 150 miles south of the planting site. At the end of the first growing season, trees in the tallest families (top 20 percent) all came from parent trees located south of the planting site (fig. 1).

Stem Crook

Although crook is an important negative character, it is difficult to measure in young walnut trees. However, we devised a crook index based on lean, number of crooks, and degree of maximum crook, and measured trees in one young plantation for this character in 1969 and 1970. In neither year were we able to detect any differences for index of crook among geographic sources. In 1969 there were differences among families within source, but not in 1970. Although this study suggests that the potential for making improvement in stem form through genetic selection is not great, it should not be ignored. In the studies reported above, the trees in the tallest families also tended to be the most crooked.

Figure 1. — *These 3-year-old (from seed) trees, growing in a seedling seed orchard in southern Illinois, are being selected and tested for desirable timber characteristics.*

SELECTING THE BEST

We have shown conclusively that walnut trees are genetically variable. The pattern of geographic variation has been useful as a guide for setting up seed-collection zones. Within collection zones the useful genetic variation that exists among trees is being discovered through progeny testing. Parent trees that prove to be genetically superior can be used as sources of improved seed and grafting stock. In progeny tests the undesirable trees (entire families and smallest trees of the better families) can be rogued and the remaining desirable trees converted to a seedling seed orchard. Cross-breeding among the desirable trees should also yield improved seed. Trees in a seedling orchard can again be progeny tested, which can lead to a second generation seed orchard. New combinations in the seed orchard may yield additional variation, with an opportunity for even more intensive selection and greater gains in the future.

FUTURE RESEARCH

Research emphasis in the future should be on finding ways to most efficiently use genetic variation that has been shown to exist. Within and outside the natural walnut range, additional provenance tests can help to define the seed-collection zone more definitively. In future tests geographic areas of seed collection can be reduced. Progeny testing from wide geographic areas may serve the dual purpose of defining more accurately the proper seed-collection zone as well as establishing the genetic worth of individual parent trees.

Obviously, we need to continue collecting data in the studies already underway. By measuring periodically we can evaluate the reliability of early recommendations. Hopefully, this will speed future research.

The effectiveness of phenotypic selection in wild populations has not been established. We need to establish tests where progeny of selected or plus trees are compared with progeny of randomly chosen individuals.

We need to determine the optimum levels of selection in seedling seed orchards. Do we want to save all the trees in the best 25 percent of the families or should we save only the best half of the trees in the best 50 percent of the families? Perhaps some other combination is best. This question needs to be answered as we begin roguing seedling seed orchards.

The selection process is confounded when both desirable and undesirable traits occur in the same tree. The problem can be solved only by compromising on one or more of the traits. We need to establish the trade-offs and pay-offs associated with selection for single traits and various combinations of traits. Solving this important problem will help us decide which traits to concentrate on in the future. We also need to know how easy or difficult it is to solve problems through silvicultural manipulation. By understanding the relative importance of genetics and silviculture, we can become more efficient in our improvement work.

The problems listed here deal primarily with describing variation and discovering the most effective and efficient methods of selection. Action programs need not wait until all these problems are solved. By taking advantage of what we presently know about seed-collection zones, nurserymen can provide faster growing seedlings today. Continuing research, running concurrently with action programs, will provide the knowledge needed to make additional improvment in walnut seedlings for the future.

REFERENCES

Bey, Calvin F. 1972. Leaf flush in black walnut at several midwest locations. Northeast. For. Tree Improv. Conf. Proc. 19: 47-51.

Bey, Calvin F. 1972. Trends in growth of walnut originating in various geographic areas. North. Nut Grow. Assoc. Annu. Rep. 62 (1971): 83-86, illus.

Bey, Calvin F., Allan S. Mickelson, and Melvin Gerardo. 1972. Black walnut seedling seed orchard development — a case history. Northeast. Area Nurserymen's Conf. Proc., p. 48-56, illus.

Bey, Calvin F., and Robert E. Phares. [n.d. Circa 1969]. Seasonal growth pattern for five sources of black walnut. Cent. States For. Tree Improv. Conf. Proc. 6: 44-47, illus.

Bey, Calvin F., John R. Toliver, and Paul L. Roth. 1971. Early growth of black walnut trees from twenty seed sources. USDA For. Serv. Res. Note NC-105, 4 p. North Cent. For. Exp. Stn., St. Paul, Minn.

Funk, David T. 1966. Seed orchards. In Black walnut culture, p. 62-65. USDA For. Serv., North Cent. For. Exp. Stn., St. Paul, Minn.

Hawker, Norman L. 1972. Variations in growth and form in young plantation black walnut (Juglans nigra L.). M.S. thesis on file in Dep. For., South. Ill. Univ., 58 p.

Parrot, Louis. 1969. [The need for a tree-breeding program for certain hardwood-forest species: applications in the genera Juglans and Acer.] For. Chron. 45(6): 386-392.

Parrot, Louis. 1971. [Climate, a selection factor in the genetic adaptation of Juglans nigra, an exotic species in Quebec, Canada.] Silvae Genet. 20(1-2): 1-9, illus.

VEGETATIVE PROPAGATION:
PROBLEMS AND PROSPECTS

R. E. Farmer, *Plant Physiologist*
Division of Forestry, Fisheries, and Wildlife Development
Tennessee Valley Authority
Norris, Tennessee

ABSTRACT.—Problems and opportunities in grafting, budding, and rooting black walnut are reviewed with emphasis on the role of these techniques in developing and using genetically improved stock. Better application of physiological principles should lead to increased production success with currently used grafting and budding procedures. Promising new information suggests that rooting will soon be a reliable technique. Some recommendations are made for future research and the development of propagation systems.

Asexual propagation of black walnut (*Juglans nigra* L.) has been the subject of much study, but is still considered difficult. In this review I hope first to show that proper application of existing physiological information should lead to greater success with some standard grafting and budding techniques, and that recent results from rooting research give new promise to this method. Second, I will present some thoughts on potentially productive approaches for future research and the application of vegetative propagation in genetic improvement and silviculture.

GRAFTING

The history of black walnut grafting is well-recorded in the annual reports of the Northern Nut Growers Association. Sitton's (1931) and O'Rourke's (1951) reviews cover early efforts, which were characterized by variation in both technique and results. A review of this early work, along with more recent studies, indicates that routine success will depend on several key factors that are thoroughly discussed in modern plant propagation texts (e.g., Hartmann and Kester 1968). In addition to good technique, attention must be given to temperature and moisture conditions conducive to rapid callus growth at the union, control of bud dormancy during union formation, and the nutritional status of stock and scion.

Some of the earliest research on black walnut grafting (Sitton 1931) established that temperatures of 25° to 28° C. and high relative humidity are necessary for rapid callus growth. It is not surprising, therefore, that outdoor grafting in the generally cool springs of the eastern United States has been frequently unsuccessful. The problem of low temperature in nursery grafting is accentuated by high root pressure, which causes sap flow or "bleeding" sufficient to prevent graft union. The 58 percent success noted by Zarger (1956) and the 70 to 80 percent reported by Lowe and Beineke (1969) for cleft and bark inlay grafts are considered to be exceptionally good under the commonly adverse field conditions. By grafting in late May when temperatures averaged 18° to 20° C., Mittempergher (1969), working in Italy, obtained 82 percent success.

Beckert (1961) has noted that root pressure can be reduced by grafting to freshly transplanted stock. Bleeding problems may also be reduced by severing tops several days before grafting or by cutting release openings in the stock below the graft (Chase 1947, Graves 1966, Hartmann and Kester 1968, Maurer 1967). In addition to these procedures for reducing root pressure, Lagerstedt and Roberts (1973) successfully used plastic covers over grafting beds to maintain temperatures suitable for callus growth of Persian walnut *(J. regia)*.

Bench grafting avoids some of the environmental problems inherent in field grafting because temperature and moisture conditions during callus formation can be easily controlled. It has long been used with some success in both winter and early spring (Kemmer 1935, 1938; Lounsberry 1937; Sitton 1931). The keys

66

to success are the induction of rapid callus growth leading to union formation, and control over bud dormancy. Late fall bench grafting using the method of Cerny (1965) is done while buds are physiologically dormant. Grafts are stored in a warm (22° to 28° C.), moist environment until callus is formed, then transferred to a cold environment (4° C.) to complete chilling requirements of buds before spring planting; Pieniazek (1972) reports up to 90 percent grafting success using this procedure in Poland. Essentially the same procedure can be used in winter and early spring if care is taken to ensure that buds, which may have completed chilling requirements, do not begin growth before callus is formed. This can be accomplished by placing grafts vertically in a sawdust-filled, cable-heated hotbed with unions exposed to 21° to 27° C. and buds exposed to chilling temperatures. Lagerstedt (1969) correctly notes that this hotbed technique is also suitable for fall grafting.

Standard spring bench grafting with entire plants exposed to warm temperature immediately after grafting has also been successful, especially under greenhouse conditions (Slate 1948, Dykstra 1971, Beck 1972, Boer 1954, Komanic 1967). Shreve has found that it is helpful to place bench grafts under intermittent mist during union formation.[1] Auxins have been used effectively to promote rapid callus formation (Brierly 1953).

While many Juglans species and hybrid graft combinations appear to be compatible during early growth (Kaeiser and Funk 1971), there is evidence of delayed incompatibility or "blackline" of *J. regia* grafted on *J. hindsii* (Serr and Forde 1959), and of *J. regia* on *J. nigra* (Glenn 1965). In Oregon the "blackline" problem has been solved through the use of "man-regian" walnut rootstock (Lagerstedt and Roberts 1973). Weschcke (1948) reports that differential growth rates eventually cause failure of *J. cinerea* on *J. nigra*. Reports of variation in grafting and budding success among genotypes suggest that intraspecific incompatibility may exist (Maurer 1967, Zarger 1945).

BUDDING

Budding, as well-described in several handbooks (e.g., Jaynes 1969, Hartmann and Kester 1968), has

---

[1] *Personal communication with Loy W. Shreve, Extension Forester, Kansas State University, Manhattan, Kansas.*

been used about as frequently as grafting in walnut propagation and is characterized by some of the same physiological problems. In addition, some difficulty has been experienced in obtaining renewed growth of the buds after successful union with stocks.

Two basic approaches have been used. First, fully developed buds in a state of imposed dormancy (i.e., chilling requirements completed and dormancy maintained by cold storage) may be grafted in spring and early summer, after which they immediately develop into shoots. Most of the more successful workers (e.g., Gerardi (1954), Becker (1964), Shelton (1954), and Chase (1947)) have used patch or chip budding. Budding in late May or June appears to be preferable to early spring budding. The advantage of this approach, of course, is that a budded plant is produced in one season by gradually reducing stock leaf surface (Becker 1964) and concentrating growth in shoots originating from grafted buds. Root pressure has been as much a problem with budding as with grafting, and procedures for its reduction have been noted above. Tuttle (1947), who used T-budding, recommended a longer than normal vertical incision in the bark to allow for drainage.

The second general approach consists of budding current-year quiescent buds in late summer. Unions are formed in summer and fall, then buds are forced the following spring. This procedure has generally been more successful than spring budding. Plate (Stoke 1937), patch (Zarger 1957, Cummings and Zarger 1945), modified-patch (Davis 1962), chip (Becker 1964), and T-budding (Gerardi 1954) all have been used. While union of the bud patch and stock plant is apparently not difficult to obtain and takes place in about 60 days (Nedev 1969), failure of buds to survive winter and to renew growth in the spring has frequently accounted for low success, especially for some interspecies budding (Davis 1964, 1965). Operational success of about 50 percent has been reported for black walnut nut-production varieties by Cummings and Zarger (1945) and Zarger (1957).

A detailed study of the relationship between budding success and the developmental stage of summer buds when taken for budding might be helpful in elucidating the causes of bud failure. For example, there may be some stages of meristem development at which budding shock may disrupt normal development and entrance into dormancy. However, it is probable that most failures are related to the slow development of callus immediately subsequent to budding and can be avoided by: (1) using stocks and bud wood of high physiological quality, and (2) careful maintenance of moisture and temperature conditions suitable for rapid callus growth. The use of auxin-like growth regulators to promote vigorous callus formation under budding conditions needs investigation.

ROOTING

Rooting black walnut cuttings has been considered very difficult, though the literature contains few reports of negative results. Recent promising efforts suggest that we may have been intimidated by the reputation of the species.

Success with trench layering has been reported for the Paradox hybrid walnut by Serr (1954), and for black walnut by Solignat and Venot (1966) and Cummins (1970), who reviewed previous work with this technique. Bey (1967) and Zatyko (1967) used the split seedling procedure to obtain genetically identical pairs. Rooting by this means, however, is relatively expensive and not readily adaptable to mass production of single genotypes.

Lynn and Hartmann (1957) rooted softwood cuttings of the Paradox walnut in a mist bed after a quick-dip treatment with indolebutyric acid (IBA). The first successful efforts with black walnut cuttings were reported by Fourcy et al. (1965) who rooted slightly etiolated juvenile shoots under mist after treatment with IBA. An adaptation of this procedure by Farmer (1971) incorporated juvenility, etiolation, girdling, and auxin treatment. Subsequent work (Farmer and Hall 1973) using auxin pretreatment of etiolated shoots produced an average of 50 to 60 percent rooting, and material from some stock plants rooted 80 to 100 percent. However, the most successful average rooting to date (about 80 percent) is that reported by Shreve and Miles (1972) using standard propagation techniques. Unetiolated physiologically juvenile cuttings were given a quick-dip IBA (5,000 to 8,000 p.p.m.) treatment and rooted in peat:perlite (1:1) under intermittent mist. Shreve and Miles emphasized that it is crucially important to obtain material originating from "adventitious" buds; i.e., those not externally visible prior to shoot elongation. Material used by Fourcy et al. (1965) and Farmer (1971) was of this origin. In preliminary trials, Shreve and Miles noted that "adventitious" shoots originating from grafted Thomas variety black walnut also rooted. Survival of rooted

cuttings has been about 75 percent, and gibberellic acid has been found to be helpful in initiating new shoot growth after rooting (Farmer 1971).

Several aspects of rooting should be investigated. First, some anatomical attention should be given to the origin of rootable shoots. While the term "adventitious" is commonly applied to shoots not originating from obvious axillary buds, it is likely that many of these shoots develop from supplemental axillary buds, not truly adventitious ones. Strictly speaking, adventitious buds arise without benefit of a connection with the apical meristem or tissue recently derived from it (Romberger 1963). Thus, rootability in walnut may be related to the stage of meristem development represented in dormant axillary buds. Both true adventitious shoots and those from suppressed axillary buds may retain the juvenile characteristics of rootability. Second, since evidence to date indicates that physiologically suitable material may be the key to rooting success, methods of producing these shoots from selected older genotypes are essential. Shreve and Miles (1972) suggest that grafted or budded shoots from such trees may be pruned or debudded to force growth of rootable shoots. Use of this technique might lead to development of stool beds or pollards for the production of selected material. Research on such a system should proceed along with further testing of shoot rootability.

Third, improved environmental conditions in the mist bed and use of chemical rooting simulators need to be incorporated into a system that will combine all factors known to enhance rooting. For example, supplemental carbon dioxide, high-intensity lighting, mineral nutrient sprays, and optimum temperatures can now easily be combined in a single mist bed. Recent success with propagation of some difficult coniferous species (Hare 1973) indicates that certain combinations of conditions can improve rooting.

USE OF VEGETATIVE PROPAGATION

Vegetative propagation by grafting and budding has long been important and economically feasible in black walnut nut culture because of a high broad-sense heritability for seed characteristics. Selection and propagation of clones with good nut qualities has been the central feature of improvement efforts. There are also reports of cloning genotypes with potential for figured wood (Bailey 1948, Wilkinson 1948, Walters 1951), though the reliability of this is still uncertain (McDaniels 1953).

More recently, vegetative propagation has been used to retain genotypes selected for their potential as parents in breeding programs aimed at improved timber production. The central feature of one breeding approach is the clonal seed orchard, or breeding arboretum, which contains a number of selections (Masters and Beineke 1973). In such a breeding situation it will be desirable, though not essential, to have clones growing on their own root systems. The major advantage of rooting will be that propagation costs should be considerably less than for grafting or budding once production systems are developed.

Systems for producing rooted cuttings may also be used directly to supply selected clones for timber production. However, breeding efforts aimed specifically at clone production will be required before attempts in this direction are made. It is unlikely that heritability for growth rate will be anywhere near as high as that for seed characteristics, and therefore clone selection for growth rate will require careful formal testing. Extensive plantings of small numbers of clones also present risks, though dangers of limited genetic variation should be less in the species mixes recommended for walnut culture than for species grown extensively in plantations (e.g., eastern cottonwood). The various problems and opportunities of forest production using clonal selections should be investigated in conjunction with current rooting research.

LITERATURE CITED

Bailey, L. F. 1948. Figured wood: a study of methods of production. J. For. 46: 119-125.

Beck, A. R. 1972. Grafting and scionwood storage. Nutshell 24(2): 4-6.

Becker, G. 1964. Further experiments bud-grafting walnut trees. North. Nut Grow. Assoc. Annu. Rep. 55: 100-103.

Beckert, W. M. 1961. Immediate grafting of transplanted black walnut stock. North. Nut Grow. Assoc. Annu. Rep. 52: 49-51.

Bey, C. F. 1967. Obtaining genetically identical black walnut seedlings. Ill. Qual. Nut Tree, Spec. Issue, Part 1 6(1): 5-8.

Boer, S. de. 1954. [Experiments on grafting walnuts, 1948-53.] Jaarb. Proefsta. Boomkwek. Boskoop 1953, p. 35-40. [Cited in For. Abstr.]

Brierly, W. G. 1953. Hormones help black walnut root grafts. Minn. Hort. 81: 44.

Cerny, L. 1965. [Grafting walnut and other woody species during the period of true winter dormancy.] Biol. Plant Acad. Sci. Bohemolson. 7(3): 226-237. [Cited in For. Abstr.]

Chase, S. B. 1947. Budding and grafting eastern black walnut. Am. Soc. Hort. Sci. Proc. 49: 175-180.

Cummins, J. N. 1970. Screen-girdling of trench-layered black walnut trees. Plant Propagator 15(4): 17-21.

Cummings, W. H., and T. G. Zarger. 1945. Nut propagation. Am. Nurseryman 81(8): 12.

Davis, B., II. 1962. The modified patch bud. Int. Plant Propagators Soc. Proc. 12: 136-139.

Davis, B., II. 1964. Nursery propagation of Carpathian walnuts. Int. Plant Propagators Soc. Proc. 14: 149-152.

Davis, B., II. 1965. A further report on English walnut bud dormancy. North. Nut Grow. Assoc. Annu. Rep. 56: 111-114.

Dykstra, C. J. 1971. Bench grafting black walnut. North. Nut Grow. Assoc. Annu. Rep. 62: 109-111.

Farmer, R. E. 1971. Rooting black walnut cuttings. Plant Propagator 17(2): 7-8.

Farmer, R. E., Jr., and G. C. Hall. 1973. Rooting black walnut after pretreatment of shoots with indolebutyric acid. Plant Propagator (In press.)

Fourcy, A., J. Lantelme, and A. Freychet. 1965. Essais sur l'enracinement des boutures de noyer. C. R. Acad. Agric. Fr., p. 21-29.

Gerardi, L. 1954. Grafting methods adapted to nut trees. North. Nut Grow. Assoc. Annu. Rep. 45: 41-44.

Glenn, E. M. 1965. Incompatibility in the walnut. East Malling Res. Stn. Annu. Rep. 53: 102.

Graves, D. L. 1966. Grafting of walnuts. Int. Plant Propagators Soc. Proc. 15: 281-284.

Hare, R. C. 1973. Environmental and chemical treatments promoting rooting of pine cuttings. Can. J. For. Res. (In press).

Hartmann, H. T., and D. E. Kester. 1968. Plant propagation — principles and practice. Ed. 2, 702 p. Englewood Cliffs, N.J.: Prentice Hall, Inc.

Jaynes, R. A., Ed. 1969. Handbook of North American nut trees. North. Nut Grow. Assoc. 421 p.

Kaeiser, M., and D. T. Funk. 1971. Structural changes in walnut grafts. North. Nut Grow. Assoc. Annu. Rep. 62: 90-94.

Kemmer, K. 1935. Veredlungsversuche mit walnussen. Gartenwelt. 38: 465-466. [Cited in Annotated bibliography of walnut and related species, USDA For. Serv. Res. Pap. NC-9, North Cent. For. Exp. Stn., St. Paul, Minn.]

Kemmer, K. 1938. Die walnussveredlung. Forsch. Sonderheft. 8: 387-389. [Cited in Annotated bibliography of walnut and related species, USDA For. Serv. Res. Pap. NC-9, North Cent. For. Exp. Stn., St. Paul, Minn.]

Komanic, I. G. 1967. [Characteristics of walnut grafting.] Izv. Akad. Nauk. Mold. Ser. biol. him. Nauk, 1966: 7, p. 30-35. [Cited in For. Abstr.]

Lagerstedt, H. B. 1969. Grafting: a review of some old and some new techniques. Int. Plant Propagators Soc. Proc. 19: 91-96.

Lagerstedt, H. B., and W. W. Roberts. 1973. Walnut grafting in Oregon — problems and solutions. North. Nut Grow. Assoc. Annu. Rep. (In press.)

Lounsberry, C. C. 1937. Bench grafting of black walnuts. North. Nut Grow. Assoc. Annu. Rep. 28: 60-63.

Lowe, W. J., and W. F. Beineke. 1969. Comparing grafting techniques for black walnut. South. Conf. For. Tree Improv. Proc. 10: 231-235.

Lynn, C., and H. T. Hartmann. 1957. Rooting cuttings under mist. Calif. Agric. 11(5): 11, 15.

McDaniels, L. H. 1953. Some aspects of the problem of curly-grained walnut. North. Nut Grow. Assoc. Annu. Rep. 44: 72-79.

Masters, C. J., and W. F. Beineke. 1973. Clonal vs. half-sib seedling orchards for black walnut. Northeast. For. Tree Improv. Conf. Proc. (In press.)

Maurer, K. J. 1967. [Problems of affinity and union in walnut grafting.] Mitt. Kosterneuburg 17: 481-491. [Cited in Annotated bibliography of walnut — Supplement No. 1. USDA For. Serv. Res. Pap. NC-70, North Cent. For. Exp. Stn., St. Paul, Minn.]

Mittempergher, L. 1969. [A new method of grafting walnuts in the nursery.] Riv. Ortoflorofruttic. 53: 189-202. [Cited in Annotated bibliography of walnut — Supplement No. 1. USDA For. Serv. Res. Pap. NC-70, North Cent. For. Exp. Stn., St. Paul, Minn.]

Nedev, N. 1969. [Studies on the duration of the stages of union in walnut budding.] Gradinarska Iozarska Nauk 6(2): 3-9. [Cited in Annotated bibliography of walnut — Supplement No. 1. USDA For. Serv. Res. Pap. NC-70, North Cent. For. Exp. Stn., St. Paul, Minn.]

O'Rourke, F. L. 1951. Factors affecting nut tree propagation. North. Nut Grow. Assoc. Annu. Rep. 42: 78-82.

Pieniazek, S. A. 1972. Autumn grafting of walnuts. Nutshell 24(3): 3, 5.

Romberger, J. A. 1963. Meristems, growth and development in woody plants. USDA Tech. Bull. 1293, 214 p.

Serr, E. F. 1954. Rooting Paradox walnut hybrids. Calif. Agri. 8(5): 7.

Serr, E. F., and H. I. Forde. 1959. Blackline, a delayed failure at the union of *Juglans regia* trees propagated on other *Juglans* species. Am. Soc. Hort. Sci. Proc. 74: 220-231.

Shelton, E. M. 1954. Patch budding black walnuts. North. Nut Grow. Assoc. Annu. Rep. 45: 37-41.

Shreve, L. M., and N. W. Miles. 1972. Propagating black walnut from rooted cuttings. Plant Propagator 18(3): 4-8.

Sitton, B. G. 1931. Vegetative propagation of the black walnut. Mich. Agri. Exp. Stn. Tech. Bull. 119, 45 p.

Slate, G. L. 1948. Grafting walnuts in the greenhouse. North. Nut Grow. Assoc. Annu. Rep. 39: 146-147.

Solignat, G., and P. Venot. 1966. Multiplication vegetative du noyer. Acad. Agri. Extrait du proces—verbal do la Seance du 25 Mai 1966, p. 674-677.

Stoke, H. F. 1937. Experiments in summer budding with walnuts. North. Nut Grow. Assoc. Annu. Rep. 28: 63-64.

Tuttle, H. L. 1947. A method of budding walnuts. North. Nut Grow. Assoc. Annu. Rep. 38: 74-76.

Walters, C. S. 1951. Figured walnut propagated by grafting. J. For. 49: 917.

Weschcke, C. 1948. The importance of stock and scion relationship in hickory and walnut. North. Nut Grow. Assoc. Annu. Rep. 39: 190-195.

Wilkinson, J. F. 1948. The grafted curly walnut as a timber tree. North. Nut Grow. Assoc. Annu. Rep. 39: 139-142.

Zarger, T. G. 1945. Nut-testing propagation and planting experience on 90 black walnut selections. North. Nut Grow. Assoc. Annu. Rep. 36: 23-30.

Zarger, T. G. 1956. Status of tree crop investigations in the Tennessee Valley region. North. Nut Grow. Assoc. Annu. Rep. 47: 47-68.

Zarger, T. G. 1957. Nursery techniques in producing nut trees. North. Nut Grow. Assoc. Annu. Rep. 48: 35-41.

Zatyko, J. M. 1967. [Vegatative propagation of the walnut variety Fertodi E.1 by way of rooting.] Acta. Agron. Acad. Sci. Hung. 16(¾): 297-302. [Cited in For. Abstr.]

TREE IMPROVEMENT ACTION PROGRAMS —
THE MISSOURI STORY

Eugene L. Brunk, *Tree Improvement Specialist*
Missouri Department of Conservation
George O. White State Forest Nursery
Licking, Missouri

ABSTRACT.—Missouri's black walnut (*Juglans nigra* L.) tree improvement action program is cooperative between the USDA Forest Service and the Department of Conservation, Forestry Division. The program consists of a long-term single tree selection-progeny test-seed orchard (SPSO) development phase, and a short-term phase. The short-term phase includes super-sized seedling production, seed collection, and seedling distribution to specific geographic zones, concurrent provenance testing, and seed production area (SPA) development.

The Missouri Tree Improvement Project was initiated in 1967 with the avowed purpose of improving the quality of the forest trees grown in Missouri through the application of known genetic principles and techniques. The primary emphasis of the program is on improving black walnut, but we also work with other species. This paper will only summarize our work with walnut.

This project is a cooperative program between the Forestry Division of the Missouri Department of Conservation and the Forest Service of the U.S. Department of Agriculture. The authority for the cooperation is contained in Title IV of the Agricultural Act of 1956. We have one forester assigned to this project on a full-time basis, but all of our foresters and nonprofessional employees are available for part-time assistance with tree improvement activities.

Approximately 80 percent of our tree improvement efforts are spent working with black walnut. Our nursery people feel that we have a demand for 500,000 walnut seedlings per year. It takes 6,000 bushels of fruit to get that many seedlings. We would like to meet this demand with improved strains of walnuts selected for fast growth, good timber form, and quality nut production in volume (fig. 1). We plan to achieve this goal primarily through the single tree selection-progeny test-seed orchard (SPSO) development process.

SPSO PROGRAM

So far, we have located, selected, and cataloged 120 superior walnut phenotypes (parent trees) in Missouri. We primarily select phenotypes that are 10 percent or more taller, are 10 percent and better in apical dominance (the proportion of total height that is a single stem), and have superior form compared to other walnut trees nearby. In addition, we select for superior nut traits and for superior volume production of nuts. Occasionally we have to select a tree because we just like the looks of it, and there are no comparisons available.

In addition to our Missouri selections, we have 12 selections from Kansas, three from Nebraska, two from Iowa, and one from Illinois. The USDA Forest Service group from Carbondale is furnishing us with 37 families from their collections of walnut for spring (1973) planting. We also have seedlings outplanted from two trees in North Carolina and from one in Tennessee. We eventually hope to test offspring from superior walnut phenotypes throughout the entire range of the species.

We have established three half-sib (having only one known parent) seedling progeny test plantations in three different geographic zones of the State. In addition, we are establishing three more test areas in two additional zones in 1973 (fig. 2). These areas will eventually total 60 acres in five different geographic zones, and we will have about 80 different families, plus several improved nut varieties, in the test areas after 1973.

Our second-year measurements of total tree height and survival have been summarized for those selections already outplanted at the three test sites. Survival of all sources has been satisfactory at all test sites. General observations of height growth indicate that southern sources have been erratic in their performance, and that northwestern sources seem to perform well when moved south and east. However, results are too unreliable at

Figure 1. — *The Missouri Tree Improvement Project is striving to produce strains of walnut trees that grow fast and develop into high quality trees such as this.*

⊗ ESTABLISHED BY 1972
○ TO BE ESTABLISHED

Figure 2. — *Walnut progeny test-seed orchard sites, Missouri Tree Improvement Project.*

this age to be definitive, so we will have to wait for the trees to grow for a while longer before we start drawing too many conclusions.

As these plantations mature, they should indicate which individuals and families of walnuts are indeed superior. We will rogue the inferior trees from the stands and will eventually have converted these test areas to seed orchards to produce seed for our nursery.

The SPSO approach is a long-term program. In order to effect some immediate improvement with walnut, we have done several other things which we think will help.

SUPER SEEDLINGS

For the last 10 years, our nurseryman has been grading-out the largest 0.1 to 1.0 percent of the nursery-run walnut seedlings, and we have been selling them as "super seedlings." These 1-0 seedlings are ⅜-inch or larger in stem diameter measured 1 inch above the root collar. The fact that these larger seedlings survive and grow better has been shown in studies conducted by the USDA Forest Service (Williams 1966; Williams 1970).

The name super seedling has been construed by some to imply genetic superiority. This is not necessarily so. Perhaps a better name for them would be super-sized seedlings, because that is what they are. No genetic superiority implied.

Our production of "supers" varies from year to year, but it averages about 6,000 seedlings per year. Our highest number was 9,000 in 1972, and we have had as few as 2,000. We would like to increase the average amount to around 10,000 per year if possible.

In addition to the super-sized seedlings, our nurseryman always tries to produce the highest possible quality in all of his walnut seedlings. Even in seedlings of known genetic origin, you must have a seedling with good buds, a balanced root-top ratio, and a satisfactory stem diameter in order to get good initial survival and growth.

SEED COLLECTION, SEEDLING DISTRIBUTION, AND PROVENANCE TESTING

In 1967, we started to collect seed by geographic zone, grow the seedlings separately, and ship seedlings back to the local zone where the seed originated (fig. 3). We are still doing this today.

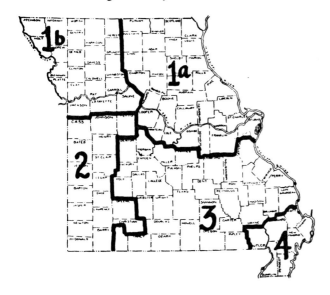

Figure 3. — *Walnut seed collection and seedling distribution zones for Missouri.*

Concurrently, we have established six provenance tests which should help us to determine if geographic races of walnut exist within the State (fig. 4). This data will aid us in deciding whether or not gains in growth can be attained by shipping seedlings out of their local zones. These tests are currently in their fourth growing season, and they have yielded some second-year data.

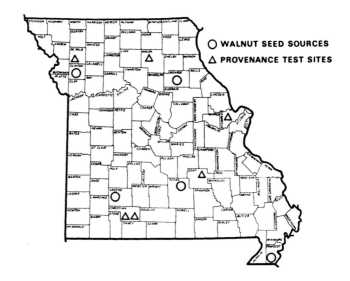

○ WALNUT SEED SOURCES
△ PROVENANCE TEST SITES

Figure 4. — *Walnut seed sources and provenance test sites, Missouri Tree Improvement Project.*

After 2 years, survival at all tests was adequate to fully stock the site. Local seed survived best in only three of six tests, and it did the poorest in two of the tests. It was average in the remaining test.

Total tree heights were quite variable, and some significant differences were found. However, we are hesitant to put much reliability in these 2-year-old trees. For the characters measured thus far, there has been no definite north-south growth pattern emerge. There might be an east-west growth pattern emerging, and the southwest prairie area seems to produce shorter trees in all zones. The definite conclusion of the tests is that we will have to wait for the trees to grow some more in order to obtain more reliable data (Brunk 1972).

SEED PRODUCTION AREA DEVELOPMENT

Another of our temporary improvement steps was initiated in 1967. We have, since that time, developed three seed production areas (SPA's) in existing walnut stands (fig. 5). These total 20 acres, and we collect seed from them whenever there is a crop. Even though we do not, necessarily, know the heredity of the SPA stands, we feel that there is some improvement in the seedlings produced, because of the roguing of inferior phenotypes from the SPA's. Seedlings from our SPA's are being tested in progeny tests, in order to compare them with seedlings from known, superior phenotypes.

73

Figure 5. — *Seed production areas, Missouri Tree Improvement Project.*

Our distribution of SPA seedlings has been even more variable than the distribution of super-sized seedlings. Some years we have not had a crop in any of the areas. In 1972, we were able to distribute 9,000 seedlings from the DuPont SPA, and in 1973 we distributed about 3,000 seedlings from the Van Meter area. We would also like to increase these amounts to at least 10,000 seedlings per year from each SPA.

THE FUTURE

Where does the Missouri program go from here? First of all, we will continue with out SPSO program. We will start cloning (reproducing vegetatively) some of our better selections because they just do not seem to want to produce any seed. Why some of these select trees do not produce seed is beyond me. Many of them appear capable of seed production...i.e., large crowns, vigorous, in a dominant position, etc. Perhaps they are too busy producing fiber, with no energy left over for sexual activity. Perhaps they produce mostly male flowers... or their flowers get killed by frost... or... they are out of a sufficient pollen flow at flowering time... or... who knows?

Our cloning procedure will probably revolve around the rooting technique as described by Shreve and Miles (1972). We will also have to do some grafting I am sure.

Eventually, we will try some hybridization work. We do not visualize much hybridization work between *Juglans nigra* L. and other *Juglans* species, but we do feel that we will try some crossing between the better selections of the native walnut.

We will probably not get into mass selection over the range of the species. This is essentially the work of the USDA Forest Service group at Carbondale, and they are better equipped for it. In all of our tree improvement activities, we always attempt to cooperate fully with other States, universities, private groups, and Federal agencies who might be doing similar work. Life is too short and our goals are many, so we cannot spend time duplicating efforts.

We will do additional provenance testing, and we will probably modify our seedling distribution plans based on our provenance tests. We will also have to modify our half-sib approach in the SPSO program because of the cloning that will be necessary in order to reproduce some of the phenotypes.

SUMMARY AND CONCLUSIONS

In Missouri, our goal in improving walnut is increased production of quality trees on the limited land base that will be available for growing trees. Ours is an action program that grows trees in the ground, and not on paper.

Our principal approach is through a single tree selection-progeny test-seed orchard development program (SPSO). In addition, we have initiated zoned seed collection and seedling distribution, the development of seed production areas (SPA), provenance testing to determine geographic variation, and distribution of super-sized seedlings for high initial survival and growth.

Our future plans call for more of the same, but with some modifications, based on our provenance and progeny tests, and on our need to reproduce superior phenotypes by cloning. We will probably do some hybridization work among *Juglans nigra* L. selections.

LITERATURE CITED

Brunk, Eugene L. 1972. Second-year results for walnut provenance tests. Study Report No. 2. 9 p. Mo. Tree Improv. Proj., Mo. Dep. Conserv.

Shreve, Loy W., and Neil W. Miles. 1972. Propagating black walnut clones from rooted cuttings. Plant Propagator 18(3): 4-7.

Williams, Robert D. 1966. Planting stock grades. *In* Black walnut culture. p. 16-17, illus. USDA For. Serv., North Cent. For. Exp. Stn., St. Paul, Minn.

Williams, Robert D. 1970. Planting large black walnut seedlings on cultivated sites. USDA For. Serv. Tree Plant. Notes 21(2): 13-14, illus.

UTILIZATION AND MARKETING OF NUTS

R. Dwain Hammons, *Vice President*
Hammons Products Company
Stockton, Missouri

ABSTRACT.—About 60 percent of commercially processed black walnut kernels are repacked for retail sale to housewives. Another 30 percent is used in ice cream, 5 percent in commercial baking, 5 percent in candy manufacture. Sterilization of nutmeats is important in ice cream manufacture. No government standards have ever been established for nutmeat sizes or quality, except for bacterial control. Recently, smaller sized nutmeats including meal have been used for retail distribution and ice cream. The annual supply of salable kernels has been reduced 40 percent in the last decade by cutting of good nut producing trees for lumber, by disease, and by indiscriminate herbicide spraying.

Just as the black walnut tree is considered the "King of the Forest," the black walnut nutmeat is thought of as the "Queen of the Kitchen." Unlike peanuts, cashews, and other table nuts, the strong flavor of black walnut kernels make them useful in the kitchen as a food flavoring ingredient.

About 60 percent of the commercially processed black walnut kernels are sold in bulk to nutmeat dealers who repack them in small 3- or 5-ounce cellophane bags for sale at the retail level to housewives for home baking purposes. Another 30 percent is used in ice cream, 5 percent in commercial baking, and 5 percent in candy.

Each ice cream manufacturer has his own variation of the basic recipe for black walnut ice cream. Most use dry nutmeats blended directly into the ice cream mix. Others prepare nutmeats in syrup. Of prime importance in the ice cream industry is strict quality and bacterial control of the nutmeats. Modern sanitary processing methods and final sterilization of the nutmeats enables the processor to guarantee a raw product free from harmful bacteria.

The 5 percent used by commercial candymakers is mostly for cream chocolate or hard candy centers; black walnut pralines and chocolate-covered black walnut clusters are also becoming a popular item.

Most black walnut kernels for commerce are packed and sold initially in 30- or 35-pound bulk cardboard cartons that are lined with a large polyethylene bag to preserve the high quality of the nutmeats. During processing the nutmeats are separated into uniform sizes by a screening process. No government standards have ever been established for sizing of black walnut kernels; however, all shellers or processors classify sizes larger than ¼ inch as large, ³/₁₆ to ¼ inch as medium, and ⅛ to ³/₁₆ inch as small. Black walnut bits or meal are also becoming a popular item. Each processor has his own quality standards to provide customer satisfaction. No State or Federal quality standards are established except for controls on bacteria.

Until recent years, most housewives preferred the large-sized nutmeats for home baking. Consequently, most of the large-sized nutmeats were packaged for retail distribution and the medium and small sizes sold to ice cream manufacturers and commercial bakers. Recently, however, partially due to higher quality of the smaller sizes and partly due to prices, all sizes including meal are now packed for retail distribution. The ice cream industry also uses all sizes, although the percentage of each size used varies from plant to plant. This trend is proving to be beneficial to the processor because he is assured of a market for all crops despite their varying sizes and yield.

The rule of thumb in the industry is that 70 percent of all nutmeats should be large, 20 percent medium, and 10 percent small. In some years, however, the nut ceases growing in early summer due to drought conditions and a greater percentage than usual are medium and small. In fact, some crops only produce 60 percent large nutmeats instead of the normal 70 percent.

Closely related to the subject of marketing of black walnut kernels is the discouraging decrease in nutmeats available each year. This decrease is largely due to the excessive cutting of the better nut producing trees for valuable lumber. An increased percent of "bad nuts" further adds to the problem. Studies have shown that *Anthracnose* disease is the biggest contributor to bad nuts and it is generally believed that indiscriminate spraying of black walnut trees with herbicides is also a cause. Consequently an increasing percent of bad nuts is harvested along with the good and sold to the processor. This has caused a year-by-year decline in the percent yield of salable nutmeats. Ten years ago a 10 percent yield was average, now about 7½ percent is expected. This reduction in yield, along with fewer trees in the nation available for nut production, has reduced the total annual supply of salable black walnut kernels by some 40 percent in the last 10 years.

From the processor's point of view the cultivation of well managed black walnut orchards and increased nut production are essential for the industry to meet the national demands for higher-quality black walnut nutmeats — the queen of the kitchen.

UTILIZATION AND MARKETING OF SHELLS

Clarence C. Cavender, *Vice President*
Hammons Products Company
Stockton, Missouri

ABSTRACT.—For years the shells from black walnuts were considered a waste product; since 65 percent of the nut is shell, disposal was a costly and difficult problem. However, research and market potential have since shown that walnut shells can be used in a variety of ways. Today black walnut shell is recognized as the best of all the nutshells and the demand has created as much of a shortage for black walnut shells as it has for the lumber and meats.

The use of the kernels from black walnuts dates back to the Indians even before our Pilgrim Fathers, but the walnut shells were for many years considered a waste product. The first recorded commercial use that I can find was for making charcoal. The charcoal from black walnut shells was of a superior quality, especially for use in gas masks during World War I. Since there were no commercial shells at that time, the demand was far greater than the supply, and the Federal government asked all farmers and roadside nut stands to save their shells for this use.

Walnut-shell flour was used in the middle 1930's as a carrying agent for various insecticides, and in 1938 a patent was issued for the use of certain sizes of ground shells in cleaning furs.

It was not, however, until 1938 and 1939 that the first important use of walnut shells was discovered. With the beginning of World War II in Europe all countries involved began to expand their airforces, and several of the allies sent their pilots to the United States for training. The additional use of so many cylinder-type airplanes placed a tremendous burden on all overhaul depots. The cleaning of pistons and cylinder heads had been done with chemicals, solvents, and hand scraping. A cheaper, faster, and better method had to be discovered and the most logical method appeared to be some type of particles in an air blast. The list of items tried ran from sand to cooked wheat. The sand was too hard and would scratch and scar. Wheat was fair but the United States government would not approve its use as it was too important a food item. Ground nutshells were tried and proved to

be the best of any tiem that had been tested. In fact, one overhaul superintendent made the remark that he thought it was the "greatest invention since women."

After the end of the war the demand and use of nutshells decreased, but their fame had spread and experiments for other uses were being conducted.

The loss of drilling fluids in drilling oil wells, especially deep wells in porous strata, has always been a problem; almost every item imaginable from cottonseed hulls to golf balls has been tried to correct it. In the late forties and early fifties, with a surplus of nutshells, someone hit on the idea of trying nutshells ground to certain sizes as an additive to the drilling mud. The results were outstanding and various patents were applied for. Some of these were issued and some were refused. Black walnut shell was recognized as far superior to any other type of nutshell for this use; however, all types were ground and are still used even though they are inferior to black walnut.

The early 1950's brought about a revolution in the automobile industry. Automatic transmissions, power steering, and power brakes were brought out. The gears in these had to be deburred, polished, and finished to a high degree to eliminate noise. Honing and finishing by hand was too slow and expensive, and with the experience of the airplane overhaul depots on carbon removal, ground nutshells were tried on automotive parts (as well as jet airplane parts). It was so successful that now black walnut shell is used to deburr, polish, descale, and finish many parts in various industries.

The utilization of the shells is now a very important part of the black walnut industry. Usable shells can be recovered from approximately 60 percent of the walnuts that are bought. After the nutmeats are extracted the shells are further broken down. This is usually done by attrition, hammer, or ball-mill methods. The shells are then screened into various sizes; the size used as an abrasive depends on the hardness and degree of finishing desired.

Some of the common uses of black walnut shells besides those already mentioned are as a filler in dynamite, a binder in glue, a marker of photograph records and other molded products, an additive in texture paint, a nonslip agent in automobile tires and on decks and slippery surfaces, a cleaner and polisher of precast concrete and mosaic tile, and a filter agent for scrubbers in smokestacks. New tests and experiments are being conducted all the time.

Truly black walnut kernels are the queen of the kitchen for nutmeats, the tree is the king of the forest for lumber, and the nutshells are the ace of all ground nutshells for any use.

When you consider the tree, the nut, and the shell, and add this to a multiple-crop concept such as a cow-calf operation with fescue or other grass, you have one of the most profitable operations in the United States today.

ORCHARD ESTABLISHMENT IN ARKANSAS

Max D. Bolar, *Forester*
Soil Conservation Service
Little Rock, Arkansas

ABSTRACT.—Although some black walnut orchards were started in earlier years, production planting for the multiple cropping of nuts, saw logs, and agricultural crops began in Arkansas Soil Conservation Districts in early 1972. Orchard sites were selected by use of the "Woodland Suitability Group" system as used by the Soil Conservation Service. Krajicek's formula was used as a basis for spacing orchards. The planting techniques described assured good survival the first year despite a drought.

Multiple cropping for nuts, saw logs, and agricultural produce is the objective of the black walnut planting program started on Arkansas Soil Conservation Districts in early 1972. This paper outlines the program and reports progress made during the first year.

In March 1972, 6,000 black walnut seedlings were planted on 210 acres of black walnut orchards in 25 counties in Arkansas on 34 ownerships. Approximately 70 percent of the planting stock was 1-0 superior black walnut seedlings provided by the Hammons Products Company Nursery at Stockton, Missouri. The remaining 30 percent was 1-0 common black walnut seedlings, obtained from the Arkansas State Forestry Commission Nursery. At the time of this writing, December 1972, orders have been received for planting over 21,000 superior seedlings on about 700 acres for 80 owners in the 1973 planting season.

SITE SELECTION

Prior to planting, sites suitable for walnut were selected using soil maps made available by the Soil Conservation Service (SCS). The following Woodland Suitability Groups[1] of the SCS were considered acceptable for walnut: 1o4, 1o7, 2o4, 2o7, 3o4, 3o7; on lower north slopes, coves, and benches 4o7; also 3f9, 3x8, and 4x8 if rockiness is moderate.

---

[1] *For an explanation of Woodland Suitability Groups see: USDA Soil Conservation Service. Soil survey interpretations for woodlands in the Boston mountains and Arkansas valley and ridges of Arkansas and Oklahoma. Progress Report W-7, RTSC, Fort Worth, Tex. 1968.*

Judgment must be exercised in the use of soils maps. Soil types may intergrade or inclusions too small to be mapped may exist. It is also possible for some soils to be too high in clay, as for example Suitability Group 2o4.

METHOD OF PLANTING

An adaptation of Krajicek's formula was used as the basis for spacing orchards.[2] The average spacing was 40 by 40 feet (27 seedlings per acre). Holes were dug with conventional farm tractors with a 3-point hitch and mounting a 14-inch-diameter soil auger. A heavy canvas blanket, 6 by 6 feet and having a 20-inch-diameter hole in the center, was laid on the planting spot. A hole was dug 30 inches deep, the soil spilling on the blanket. After the hole was dug about half of the soil was funneled back into the hole with the blanket. The seedling, with roots averaging about 15 inches long, was held at the root collar by the planter, who stepped down into the hole and tamped the soil with his feet while his helpers funneled the remainder of the soil into the hole.

GRASS AND WEED SPRAYS

After planting a spray mixture was applied in 4-foot-diameter circles around the planted seedling. A section of stove pipe was placed over the seedling during the spraying operation to protect it from the spray and possible ill effects. The mixture used was: ¾ ounce simazine,

---

[2] *John E. Krajicek. Growing space requirements. In Black walnut culture. 94 p., illus. North Cent. For. Exp. Stn., St. Paul, Minn. 1966.*

2 ounces dalapon, ½ fluid ounce 2,4-D amine, 1 teaspoon of low-sudsing detergent, and 1 gallon of water.[3]

SURVIVAL

In early September 1972 the survival count was about 93 percent. Only half the normal amount of rain fell during the growing season causing a severe drought and apparently an early leaf fall. It is believed that some persons making survival counts judged that seedlings that lost their leaves early were dead. In view of this, survival may have been even better than 93 percent.

AGRICULTURAL CROPS

Although most owners of the Arkansas plantings used 40- by 40-foot spacings, one owner used 48 by 48 and another used 35 by 35 in order to clean-till crops intended for planting between the rows. Six of the 34 planters had planned to use clean-tilled crops — primarily soybeans. However, due to an early drought all but one of them left their land fallow. Most of the planters used the area between the trees for meadow. None pastured their orchards because the trees lacked protection against livestock.

In the 1972 and 1973 plantings about 10 percent of the owners will plant clean-tilled crops between the trees for several years and then will change these areas to meadow. The balance of the owners will use meadow for 9 or 10 years; about half of these will pasture their orchards. One owner is considering planting Christmas trees in his orchard. The trees immediately adjacent to the walnuts will be the first ones thinned.

JUSTIFICATION FOR WIDE SPACING

Some consider the 40- by 40-foot spacing too wide. However, the following objectives are given to justify wide spacing:

1. Maximize diameter growth to obtain a fast-growing butt log 12 to 16 feet in length.

2. Maximize nut production by having large, spreading crowns.

3. Provide space between trees to grow an agricultural crop for income while awaiting log and nut production.

4. Obtain brush control by virtue of multiple cropping with agricultural crops.

5. Eliminate necessity of precommercial thinning as with closely spaced trees.

6. Reduce the rotation age and thus reduce the compound interest of the carrying charges for planting and improvement.

The above objectives more or less follow the premises made by Wylie that wide-spaced, short-boled, wide-crowned walnut trees produce greater nut crops and have faster diameter growth than closely spaced trees.[4]

Although it is too early to evaluate multiple cropping and wide spacing from our 1972 Arkansas experience, our planting techniques seem to have assured good survival despite the unusually dry growing season.

---

[3] *See page 114.*

---

[4] *John E. Wylie. Nuts and wood – dual crops for management. In Black walnut culture. 94 p., illus. North Cent. For. Exp. Stn., St. Paul, Minn. 1966.*

VEGETATION MANAGEMENT INCREASES PRODUCTION IN NUT ORCHARD

Harvey A. Holt, *Assistant Professor*
and
Jack E. Voeller, *Research Assistant*
Arkansas Agricultural Experiment Station
Fayetteville, Arkansas

ABSTRACT.— Tree growth, nut production, nut weight, and nut size were substantially increased by controlling vegetation with herbicides. The response to varying degrees of vegetation control has been consistent for the first 2 years of the study. Because of the magnitude of response, controlling vegetation appears to be a cost of orchard management that will prove profitable over the long run.

Considerable research has been done on the control of mixed hardwood species in new black walnut (*Juglans nigra* L.) plantations. In contrast, the study reported here was made to learn the impact of grass control on the tree growth and nut characteristics of established, nut-bearing trees. The study was started in 1971.[1] Results after two growing seasons are reported.

METHODS AND MATERIALS

The walnut plantation studied is located near Vaughn, Arkansas, in the northwest corner of the State. It was established in 1963 and replanted in the following years until a uniform plantation with a 50- by 50-foot spacing was obtained. The plantation trees are Thomas variety grafted to native black walnut rootstock. The seedlings were grafted at age three and held in the nursery until age five. The first substantial nut production occurred in 1970.

The soil is a Razort gravelly silt loam, moderately fertile, alluvial, derived from limestone, and containing 15 to 35 percent chert gravel. The test trees are located in a field of perennial fescue (*Festuca* sp.) which yields one to two cuttings of hay or about 80 to 100 bales per acre per cutting. The soil is tested annually and fertilized according to recommendations for the fescue grass.

[1]*H. A. Holt and J. E. Voeller. Effect of vegetation control on established black walnuts. Ark. Farm Res. 21(1): 8. 1972.*

Twenty-five trees were selected for study. Five trees were assigned systematically to each of five treatments. Each tree was at the center of an 8- by 8-foot plot. The treatments were (1) diuron, (2) simazine, (3) terbacil, (4) total vegetation control, and (5) no vegetation control (check). The three herbicides were all applied at the rate of 3 pounds active material per acre. Only one application of herbicide was made each year accompanied by 1 pound of paraquat per acre. Total vegetation control was achieved by applying paraquat, 1 pound per 100 gallons of water, at monthly intervals with a garden sprayer. The check plots received no treatment. Herbicides were applied with a portable plot sprayer to assure accurate amounts.

Treatments began May 3, 1971; retreatment at the same rate was made April 17, 1972. The herbicides were selected to create a spectrum of vegetation control for evaluation of its effect on the trees. The percent of vegetation control was subjectively estimated at monthly intervals from initial treatment to September. An addition to the treatment series was made in 1972. On July 20, all the terbacil, simazine, and diuron plots were resprayed with 2,4,5-T amine, 4 pounds per 100 gallons of water, with a garden sprayer for broadleaf control. Blackberries and poison ivy were becoming particularly noticeable in some of the plots.

Both limb length and trunk diameter were measured as indices of growth response. After leaf abscission, a "best" accessible limb, one season's growth, was measured on each tree. Beginning in 1972, the tree's diameter growth was measured at a permanently marked point on each tree at about 2 feet from the ground. Because of the low branching present in the trees, this height was used rather than diameter at breast height. The first measurement was made in April at the time of treatment and the final measurement after leaf abscission in November.

In October of each year the nuts were collected and immediately hulled. The fresh weight yield (for which the individual is paid) was measured for each tree. Each year, up to 10 nuts from each tree were ovendried, measured for size, and cracked for kernel yield. In 1971, volume was estimated by measuring diameters of the nuts; in 1972, nut volume was determined by water displacement. The ovendry weights of each nut and the kernel weight after cracking were measured for determining percent kernel yield.

RESULTS

The results of vegetation control in 1972 agree with the 1971 results. Although the actual numbers change, the trends are consistent. The greater the vegetation control the greater the limb length (table 1). Limb length on trees having no vegetation (total "control") was more than 300 percent over the limb length on check trees. Even the limb length of trees with the least vegetation control exceeded the limb length of check trees by more than 180 percent.

Table 1.—*Influence of vegetation control on limb length and trunk diameter, 1972*

Treatment	Average vegetation control	Growth	
		Limb length	Trunk diameter
	Percent	Inches	Inches
Check	0	7.7	0.26
Simazine	40	21.7	.44
Diuron	42	21.2	.47
Terbacil	86	24.5	.50
Total control	100	32.3	.66

Diameter growth for 1972, as with limb growth, constantly increased with increasing vegetation control (table 1). The least degree of vegetation control yielded nearly a 70 percent increase in diameter growth. Diameter growth of trees with no vegetation exceeded diameter growth of check trees by more than 150 percent. Nearly all trees treated with herbicide grew more than the fastest growing check tree.

The number of nuts was greater in 1972 than in 1971 for all treatments. This is a result of a higher proportion of the trees bearing in 1972 which, in turn, may be a reflection of tree maturity. Nut sizes, fresh weight, and ovendry weight were consistently less than in 1971; percent kernel yield was greater than in 1971. The smaller sizes may result partly from the different ways of determining volume, but may also reflect the extremely dry summer of 1972.

Except in one case, controlling vegetation with herbicides increased the numbers, sizes, and weight of nuts (table 2.) For trees growing in plots in which all vegetation was controlled, average nut sizes were 35 percent greater than on check plots. Even the least effective herbicide treatment resulted in a 19 percent increase in nut size. The various treatments increased fresh nut weight an average of 11 to 17 percent over the check trees.

DISCUSSION

The increased tree growth and nut production measured in this trial are perhaps attributable to several factors. The study trees are directly competing with fescue. There is evidence to suggest that grasses are more competitive, particularly for moisture, than other plant species. The field in which these trials are located is also fertilized annually after soil testing. Controlling the vegetation around the trees would tend to make both fertilizer and moisture more available to the trees. The summer drought common in this area may tend to increase response to available moisture. These factors are mentioned only to provide a context within which to interpret out results.

For the orchard owner, two items are of particular importance. One is the growth of the trees as related to vegetation control, which we have already discussed. The second, and perhaps the most important, is the nut yield during the productive life of the orchard. While there are some inconsistencies in the results, one factor is very obvious — vegetation control for the 2-year period increased nut production — both numbers and fresh weight (table 3). The untreated trees produced both fewer nuts and fewer pounds of nuts during both years than any of the vegetation control treatments.

Although the difference in nut numbers between the check trees and next best treatment was only 7 percent, the difference in pounds was a substantial 28 percent due to the larger size and weight of nuts. Obviously,

Table 2.—*Influence of vegetation control on selected nut characteristics, 1972*

Treatment	Average vegetation control	Total nuts	Nut size	Fresh nut weight	Ovendry nut weight	Kernel yield
	Percent	No.	Cu. in.	Ounces	Ounces	Percent
Check	0	716	1.12	0.75	0.54	27
Simazine	40	792	1.38	.88	.64	27
Diuron	42	495	1.46	.83	.68	27
Terbacil	86	1,602	1.33	.84	.62	28
Total control	100	929	1.52	.88	.69	25

Table 3.—*Cumulative nut yields per tree after 2 years of treatment*

Treatment	Average nuts	Ave. fresh weight of nuts
	No.	Lbs.
Check	151	7.14
Simazine	199	11.36
Diuron	162	9.12
Terbacil	337	19.06
Total control	208	11.69

this 28 percent increase is more important because nuts are sold by weight. Other comparisons, even more dramatic in nature, could be made; however, it is not the object of this report to recommend specific herbicides, rather only to point out the importance of controlling vegetation adjacent to the trees. The results are not particularly related to degree of control but do highlight the importance of vegetation control.

Our treated plots are only 0.0015 acre in size per tree; at the suggested spacing of 40 by 40 feet or 27 trees per acre, only 0.04 acre would be treated. The plot size used in this trial is not suggested as optimum but is just the size that we chose to treat. The treated area is a miniscule part of the total land area. Because of the small treated area per acre, the cost of herbicide per tree at the rates we used is only about 1 cent per tree. Assuming a minimal value of 4 cents per pound for the nuts, an increase in nut production of only one-fourth pound per year would pay for the herbicide. Our results indicate that the increased nut yield greatly exceeds that

amount. We would suggest that, even for this plantation just beginning nut production, the increases we have obtained would more than pay for the cost of material and cost of application. The increased growth of the trees and an increased future production is net profit.

The impact of the increased diameter growth also deserves some elaboration. Growth on the trees receiving total control indicates that veneer size walnut logs can be grown in half the time required by the check trees. The partial control treatments shorten the rotation age by more than a third of that required by the untreated trees. This has important ramifications not only for walnut grown in orchards but also for walnut grown in plantations for timber production.

A word of caution is also in order. Simazine and paraquat are the only herbicides in this study presently registered for use in nut-bearing walnut orchards. Terbacil and diuron were included to provide a spectrum of vegetation control for measuring plant response; this report *DOES NOT* recommend or suggest their use (see page 114).

Tree growth, nut production, nut weight (both fresh and ovendry), nut size, and percent kernels were all increased by vegetation management. Although this study is very limited in size, the data indicate very large and consistent responses to vegetation control over the 2 year period. Results in other areas, on different soils, or with different competing species, may be substantially different. We do feel, however, when operating under the multiple cropping concept with grasses as the competing species, vegetation control should be included in the total management program.

BLUEGRASS SOD AND TREES

Jack Weeks, *Weeks Walnut Farm*
Pleasant Hill, Missouri

ABSTRACT.—Profit was my motive when I planted 80 acres of black walnuts 11 years ago. Since then I have learned a great deal about walnuts and as yet have received no profit; however, I harvested 8,600 pounds of fine-quality nuts last year. I expect to start making a small profit in the next 2 or 3 years.

Using bluegrass as a second crop in the orchard has allowed me to receive a reasonable return on the land while the trees grow into bearing and will play a great part in the future profits from this operation.

When I first became interested in making a planting of black walnut I owned no farm or other land, so the first order of business was to acquire suitable land for an orchard.

At first I looked at the cheapest land available, and soon found that the reason it was cheap was because it was very poor land — mostly rough and unfit for walnuts or anything else. One tract of 120 acres I looked at was very good land — nearly all tillable — with 60 acres of good bluegrass pasture. It was priced at $400 per acre. Since this was considerably more than I had expected to pay, I was not interested in this farm at first. However, the more I looked at hilly and eroded land — cut up with ditches and overgrown with brush — the more I thought about the good 120 acres at the higher price, and looking at that 60 acres of bluegrass I began to get an idea how I might be able to buy this farm. I contacted a landscaper and got a bid of $225 per acre for the sod that could be harvested from this pasture. About 40 acres of it was salable.

I talked to several farmer friends about the feasibility of planting bluegrass for a sod crop. They were unanimous in their opinion that it couldn't be done — that it would take at least 5 years to produce a sod crop and the bluegrass would have to be planted with a nurse crop of alfalfa or clover. What they were doing was trying to tell me I couldn't do something I didn't know anything about; this was just the challenge I needed, so I bought the farm and immediately started to prove them wrong.

I planted 80 acres of walnut trees and started harvesting the grass that was salable and began to prepare the remaining 60 acres of land for seeding bluegrass. Since I felt if you wanted to raise popcorn you wouldn't plant peanuts, I omitted the nurse crop and just planted bluegrass.

I was lucky with my first crop in that we had almost perfect weather and rainfall. In spite of much less than perfect planting we got a good stand of grass. The next year my mistakes began to catch up with me, and after making several mistakes that cost several thousands of dollars I became a very apt student of bluegrass culture. I am now happy to be able to say my methods and results have steadily improved over the years.

Ten years ago the bluegrass business was very much like the walnut business — you could get lots of advice from anyone you asked. The trick was to sort out the very small amount that was any good and would apply to my operation. I soon found that in the bluegrass business some specialized equipment was necessary. I built most of it myself or modified available equipment to do a special job.

In the beginning I was doing well to obtain a sod crop every 3 years from the same ground. Later I was able to step this up to every 2 years. In 1972 I harvested grass that was planted in the fall of 1971 — a 12-month crop; however, I feel that with timely rains a crop every 18 months will be about the best that can be expected on the average. As I improved my methods and produced a better grade of sod, the price went up. The first grass I sold brought $225 per acre. The last I sold brought $500 per acre.

While the selling price of turf has gone up, the cost of producing it has also increased. At first I was spending about $75 to $80 to produce an acre of turf. It now costs about $160 per acre. The production costs have increased because of better seedbed preparation; using 40 pounds of seed per acre instead of 20, and using a great deal more fertilizer, more frequent mowing, and also spraying to control broadleaf weeds.

The net return using bluegrass as a second crop in my orchard is now about $100 per acre per year. As long as this return remains at this level, I feel it is necessary to charge but a small amount of land investment to the trees and this will reflect in increased profits from the nut crop.

Because of my location — close to a market — bluegrass turf has proved to be a good choice for a second crop with walnut. In fact, it has proved so profitable I have leased an additional 120 acres for production of turf. I now expect to sell about $40,000 worth of turf each year. This causes me to whistle louder as I go to the bank.

There are other benefits from turf in an orchard. Both walnut and bluegrass respond well to high applications of nitrogen. With good turf underfoot, it is possible to get into the orchard with spray equipment in wet weather to better time the spray applications. The same applies to nut-picking time. You can move in on turf where otherwise wet ground might keep you out.

There are many problems with raising grass, but with good management they can be overcome, and a walnut orchard planted with bluegrass and kept well-mowed is one of the most pleasing sights you will ever see.

FORAGE AND TREES

Alan King, *King Farms, Inc.*
Dadeville, Missouri

ABSTRACT.—The use of walnut trees in a concept known as multiple cropping more fully utilizes the productivity of the land. Growing forage in the interim required for trees to mature seems to offer a logical use of medium- to high-cost cropland while sustaining trees as a secondary crop. The trees will gradually change from the secondary crop to the primary crop as they grow in size.

MULTIPLE CROP CONCEPT

The idea of multiple crops is not new to many farms in this area. We at King Farms, Inc. have utilized the same acreage for pasturing livestock; growing small grain; and harvesting grass seed, legume seed, and hay — all in the same year.

The use of walnut trees as a part of a multiple-crop plan seems logical to us. Trees can be grown on a certain number of our acres being used for hay and pasture. We plan to be flexible as to whether the use in the early years will be pasture or hay.

We do know what income we can expect from the hay and pasture during the first few years, and the additional costs of maintaining the walnut trees will be primarily absorbed as extra time and labor of family members.

We feel these "extras" are important to making the overall operation a profitable one. We expect to continue the application of commercial fertilizer at the current cost of $14 per acre per year or more, plus a limestone application every few years.

We have little experience in tree management but expect to be flexible enough in our future plans to adapt recommendations uncovered by research. We are confident the rate of walnut growth and production will be increased through research in the next few years and feel that the time to get started on a project of this type is now, instead of waiting to see for sure if it will work. A promise that it will work always breeds enough competition to lower the profit potential.

The use of land for cattle grazing requires careful management to realize a practical profit.

We must consider our ability to compete with other types of soil in walnut cropping. We know how to make comparisons of land productivity for growing grass through personal observation and actual research in terms of pounds of forage per acre, animal units per acre, or even pounds of beef per acre. In our operation the animal-unit method of comparison seems most reasonable because we deal primarily with breeding livestock, where sales cannot consistently be measured on a by-the-pound basis.

The land purchased at today's prices must produce more than natural grass in order to return even a small percentage on the investment. Taxes, maintenance, and overhead, all can be expected to increase.

The land where the 80 acres of walnuts are planted was part of a 500-acre tract purchased in about 1960 for $74 per acre. The land was unimproved with a moderate amount of brush. Each 10 acres would support a cow-calf unit per year. A complete renovation, which cost approximately half the original land price, has increased the capacity to 3 acres per cow-calf unit. This capacity is made possible by $14 per acre per year commercial fertilizer-lime costs.

We are planning to increase this cost as we have on other land to $15 to $18 per acre, which will enable us to carry the cow-calf unit on 2 to 2¼ acres. Of course, this is all useless unless we concentrate on the cows' ability to calve and produce more beef per pound of forage.

The land today would cost at least $350 per acre, which gives a cost per acre for interest alone of $26. When we plug in a cow-calf unit investment of $350 we must have $36 per acre return for fixed overhead before we allocate cost to fertilizer, labor, machinery, etc.

Since the variables become so great at this point I prefer to show the growth of grass on our land as follows:

	Dollars per acre
Interest on land ($350/acre)	26
Annual fertilizer treatment	16
Taxes and Maintenance	2
Total expenses	44
Production of 5,000 lbs. forage at $20/ton net	50
Optional returns fescue seed 300 lbs./acre at $.80/lb. net	24
Total income	74

Normal production of forage, beef, or most any farm product is seldom highly profitable within itself. It is the options that make the success, such as the fescue seed crop. This is the reason we are seeking walnut trees as another "complementary option."

Cropping by today's methods usually requires efficient equipment and a definite plan or pattern. The owner who undertakes multiple cropping must select his site with his future cropping plans and machinery type in mind. A field that is undesirable for hay or row crops will be even less desirable after the planting of walnut trees. And farming around the trees seems to amplify the problems presented by obstacles such as stones, ditches, terraces, and irregular surfaces.

It is very easy to place the trees in the ground with decreasing accuracy as the hours of planting wear on; however, a few inches variance can become a great obstacle to a specialized piece of equipment over the period of years that the tree will be one of the crops.

Getting the most from the acre of land while practicing good conservation seems to be the name of the game. We plan to continue growing grass; the addition of trees should not lower the economic value of the grass until the trees themselves can begin to contribute to the income per acre of land. We do not consider the walnut plantings an economic gamble, but a conservation-type investment of "future faith."

DISEASES

Frederick H. Berry, *Principal Plant Pathologist*
USDA Forest Service, Forest Insect and Disease Laboratory
Northeastern Forest Experiment Station
Delaware, Ohio

ABSTRACT.—Several diseases that can cause considerable damage to black walnut trees are discussed. Walnut root rots are serious in a number of nurseries where black walnuts are grown. Anthracnose is the most serious foliage disease of black walnut, and some methods for its control are suggested. Other diseases discussed include walnut bunch, heart rots, and cankers.

Black walnut is host to a large number of disease organisms. The "Index of Plant Diseases" (USDA 1960), lists more than 50 disorders of this tree species. Fortunately, most of these are not serious and cause little, if any, economic loss. There are, however, several diseases that walnut growers need to be aware of because on occasion they do cause considerable damage.

ROOT ROTS

Root rots are the most widespread problem with black walnut nursery stock. They occur to some extent in almost all nurseries where black walnuts are grown. These root rots apparently can be caused by several different soil fungi.

A root rot caused by the fungus *Phytophthora citricola* has been responsible for serious losses at the Jasper-Pulaski State tree nursery in Indiana (Green and Pratt 1970). Initial infection occurs in the seedbeds, usually in spots or patches. The diseased walnut seedlings are killed in the seedbed, or infection may continue to develop in overwinter storage and cause losses in the spring during handling and shipping. The first visible symptom of the disease is a wilting of the more succulent parts of the tops, followed by blackening of the entire plant. Examination of these infected plants reveals that most of the roots are dead or dying, and water-soaked lesions usually are visible at the root collar (fig. 1). Soil moisture is critical for infection, and the disease is usually more severe after periods of heavy rain or high soil moisture levels.

Figure 1 — *Root rot of black walnut seedlings infected with* Phytophthora citricola.

Other tree nurseries have reported a similar root rot of black walnut seedlings. *P. citricola* was also isolated from diseased walnut roots from the Green Springs State Nursery in Ohio,[1] and *P. cactorum* was isolated from walnut seedlings that suddenly wilted and died in a North Carolina nursery (Crandall and Hartley 1938).

Walnut seedlings at the Vallonia tree nursery in Indiana developed a stem and root condition similar to that described for *Phytophthora. Fusarium episphaeria* was isolated with regularity from the root portions of these seedlings.[2] The pathogenicity of this *Fusarium*

---

[1] *Personal communication with Robert G. Linderman, September 21, 1972.*

[2] *Personal communication with Frederick M. Rothwell, August 30, 1972.*

species was determined by artificially inoculating the fungus into roots of healthy walnut seedlings.

Soil fungi associated with walnut root rot in other nurseries include *Cylindrocarpon radicicola, C. candidum, Pythium vexans,* and *Cylindrocladium* sp.

Fumigation of nursery seedbeds does not control walnut root rot since these soil-borne pathogens are often carried in from unfumigated areas.

Some degree of control can be attained by avoiding areas in seedbeds where the drainage is poor and surface water may stand. Methods of direct control by chemicals or other means need to be investigated.

The disease is considered an important limiting factor in production of black walnut nursery stock. And when seedlings with root rot are outplanted, they often do not survive.

ANTHRACNOSE

The most serious foliage disease of black walnut is anthracnose, caused by the fungus *Gnomonia leptostyla*. This disease may quickly reach epidemic proportions during wet weather in the growing season and cause many walnuts — from seedlings to mature trees — to lose almost all their leaves by midsummer. This premature defoliation slows growth, weakens trees, and sometimes kills them. And the dark, shriveled kernels from diseased trees are usually not viable.

Black walnut trees vary in their susceptibility to walnut anthracnose. But during rainy seasons even the less susceptible trees become severely infected and defoliated.

Leaves, nuts, and occasionally shoots of the current season's growth are all attacked by the fungus. Tiny dark brown or black spots appear on infected leaves (fig. 2). Gradually these spots become more numerous, enlarge, and often merge to form still larger dead areas. Yellowish- to golden-leaf tissue usually borders these areas.

Sunken necrotic spots, smaller than those on the leaves, appear on husks of infected nuts. When immature nuts become diseased, they do not develop properly and many drop prematurely.

Figure 2. — *Anthracnose lesions on a black walnut leaf. Causal agent is* Gnomonia leptostyla.

No practical control of anthracnose is known for walnut trees growing under forest conditions. In nurseries, control of the disease can be accomplished by periodic spraying of the walnut seedlings with fungicides. Zineb and maneb have given satisfactory control at the rate of 2 pounds per 100 gallons of water.[3] To protect the seedlings it is necessary to apply the first spray when leaves are about one-half mature size, followed by two or three additional sprayings at biweekly intervals.

Recently, an experimental fungicide, triarimol, has shown promise of controlling walnut anthracnose in Ohio nursery beds.[4] Further studies are in progress to test its effectiveness.

---

[3] *See page 114.*

[4] *Personal communication with Winand K. Hock, October 15, 1972.*

WALNUT BUNCH

This disease was once thought to be caused by a virus. However, recent studies have shown mycoplasmalike organisms regularly associated with diseased trees.[5] Mycoplasmas appear to be the smallest living organisms, somewhat larger than viruses, but smaller than bacteria. Though mycoplasmas have been known to cause disease in animals for many years, they have been discovered in plants only recently.

Bunch disease is known to be present throughout the eastern United States. Concern over possible spread of the disease to the West Coast resulted in California's placing a quarantine on the importation of walnut nursery stock from east of the Rocky Mountains.

Besides black walnut, bunch disease has been found on butternut, Japanese walnut, and Persian (English) walnut. Japanese walnut is most susceptible, and black walnut seems to be most resistant. Symptoms on black walnut are often so mild that diagnosis is difficult, and some trees may be symptomless carriers.

The most characteristic feature of bunch disease is the tendency of axillary buds to grow rather than to remain dormant. This growth produces tightly packed bunches of small wiry shoots and undersized leaves. The diseased shoots do not go into dormancy in the fall and are susceptible to cold injury.

The wood of diseased trees becomes very brittle, branches die back, and highly susceptible trees are often killed. Affected trees set few nuts and those that mature are usually soft-shelled and poorly developed.

Control of bunch disease is difficult because means of spread and method of infection are unknown. Removal of diseased branches from black walnut trees may be practical because this species seems to be less seriously affected than other walnut species, and diseased trees have been known to recover naturally. No infected trees should be allowed to remain in the vicinity of walnut nurseries.

OTHER DISEASES

Several species of heart-rot fungi cause decay of the heartwood of black walnut. Two of the most common

heart-rotters are the "false tinder" fungus *Fomes igniarius* and the "sulphur fungus" *Polyporus sulphureus*. These fungi usually gain entry through wounds or dead branch stubs. No direct method of controlling heart rots is known. Initial infections can be kept at a minimum by maintaining tree vigor and preventing wounding.

Cankers on black walnut trees caused by the fungus *Nectria galligena* have a characteristic target appearance, resulting from a perennial killing of bark tissues by the fungus in the autumn and growth of host callus material in spring or early summer. Although few cankered trees are killed, the quality and quantity of lumber or veneer produced from them is often lowered. On good sites cankers tend to heal, while on poorer sites the rate of canker enlargement often surpasses the healing rate. All badly diseased trees should be felled and the cankered tissues cut out and burned.

A basal stem canker disease has been found recently in walnut plantations in Indiana, Illinois, and Missouri. Bark and cambial tissues are killed in the cankered area, which is just above the ground line. Eventually the canker encircles the stem, translocation of materials upward from the roots is interrupted, and the crown dies. Dead and dying trees are colonized by ambrosia beetles, and one of the first indications that a tree may be cankered is the appearance of tiny "pin holes" in the stem, from which insect frass is extruded. Research is in progress to determine the cause of the disease.

RESEARCH NEEDS

There is a definite need for more research on diseases of black walnut. Many problems still need to be solved. For example, new environmentally acceptable control measures are urgently needed for walnut root rot. And as black walnut plantings increase, new disease problems will assuredly appear.

LITERATURE CITED

Crandall, Bowen S., and Carl Hartley. 1938. *Phytophthora cactorum* associated with seedling diseases in forest nurseries. Phytopathology 28: 358-360.

Green, R. J., Jr., and R. G. Pratt. 1970. Root rot of black walnut seedlings caused by *Phytophthora citricola*. Plant Dis. Rep. 54: 583-585.

U. S. Department of Agriculture. 1960. Index of plant diseases in the United States. U. S. Dep. Agric., Agric. Handb. 165, 531 p.

---

[5] *Personal communication with Carl E. Seliskar, March 28, 1972.*

INSECTS AS RELATED TO WOOD AND NUT PRODUCTION

William E. Miller, *Principal Insect Ecologist*
North Central Forest Experiment Station

ABSTRACT.—The more important insects affecting wood and nut production are named and briefly discussed. Wood crop insects mar tree form or impair incremental growth by retarding or spoiling it. Walnut production practices may at times unintentionally increase insect numbers. Nonchemical control or regulation measures are highlighted. New information about insects is not keeping pace with progress in other aspects of walnut production technology.

Little new knowledge about black walnut insects has accumulated in the 7 years since the report by Hay and Donley (1966) at the Walnut Workshop. My presentation mainly exploits old information and allied experience outside walnut culture. Neglect of protection research may prove costly by slowing progress toward ideal production technology.

Walnut protection can be divided into the following categories, which are listed in descending order of existing knowledge: (1) developing nut crops, (2) developing wood crops, (3) nuts in storage, and (4) developing nursery stock. While convenient, these categories do overlap somewhat. For example, some insects that reduce nut production also reduce wood increment; some that feed in developing nuts continue feeding after nuts are stored.

The first two categories will be elaborated here; the last two will be omitted because there is too little knowledge for a meaningful discussion about insects that attack nuts in storage or developing nursery stock.

Measures for direct insect control or direct regulation will be detailed here only when nonchemical in mode of operation. Pesticides are subject to rapid improvement and change in official registration. Local extension representatives should be consulted for current recommendations. Several measures for regulating insects indirectly by warding them off instead of killing them will be noted. Though overshadowed by pesticide technology, these indirect measures suggest that more could be developed.

DEVELOPING NUT CROPS

Walnuts, like other seeds, are an energy-rich food source for insects as well as humans. More information is available about Persian walnut insects in the West than about black walnut insects in the East. A few insects affect both. The main ones now associated with nut crops of black walnut are:

1. Curculio or weevil (*Conotrachelus retentus*). Adults feed and lay eggs in immature nuts. Larval offspring then consume nut contents. The life cycle normally lasts 1 year (univoltine) (Schoof 1942). Foliage sprays applied after pollination are said to regulate the weevil. Nonchemical regulation is also possible in isolated plantings by promptly destroying nuts that drop prematurely. Such nuts contain a new weevil brood (Johnson 1969).

2. Husk fly (*Rhagoletis suavis*). The larvae or maggots can cause discoloration and off-taste of nut meats. Quality rather than production is affected. The insect can be regulated with foliage sprays containing contact or systemic pesticides with or without attractants (Nickel and Wong 1966, Johnson 1969).[1] The life cycle is univoltine. Because time of adult appearance varies, fly trapping is important for scheduling pesticide applications. The design and use of a simple fly trap are explained by Johnson (1969). Husk fly damage may be lessened nonchemically if late-maturing walnut varieties are cultured because the flies cannot successfully lay eggs when husks are hard (Johnson 1969).

Mites, aphids, and foliage-eaters may reduce nut production when their populations become high (Michelbacher and Ortega 1958). Since their feeding also reduces wood increment, these arthropods will be discussed in the wood crop category.

[1] *See page 114.*

91

Insect-caused nut losses have not been deliberately searched out nor scientifically evaluated. Awareness of the above nut feeders is due mostly to capsulized grower experience. Nut-life tables derived from systematic observations of crop development from pollination onward could reveal overlooked or over-rated insect problems (Harcourt 1970). In the only study approaching this type I know of, 205 immature nuts on five black walnut trees in an Illinois orchard were tagged and their survival recorded.[2] Seventy percent of the tagged nuts never reached maturity. Their fate is unknown but insect intervention was likely. Close study of developing seed crops almost always implicates insects as a bibliography like Barcia and Merkel (1972) reveals.

Decisions whether to regulate insects that directly affect nut production will depend on whether the objective is to maximize nut production, stem volume, or a dual crop. Short logs and long crowns are recommended in dual-crop culture in contrast to wood production alone; large crowns produce more nuts and larger stem increments (Wylie 1966). Nevertheless, regulation of nut feeders increases nut biomass at the expense of other tree increments, including that of the stem. Reductions in radial stem increment and other vegetative growth accompany years of intense reproductive growth in many tree species (Matthews 1963). Current-year biomass distribution among black walnut tree parts remains to be fully examined, but tentative estimates are available from the work of Schneider (1970). Schneider measured biomass of different aboveground parts of 31-year-old black walnut trees. When converted to current-year values (for stems, dividing total stem biomass by years of tree age), the additions to stem and nuts amounted to about 20 and 4 percent, respectively, of total current biomass accumulation. Schneider termed the year of his observations a light nut year. In a heavier nut year, nut crop and stem-increment biomass may be more nearly equal. These relationships need elucidation to facilitate decisionmaking about nut insect regulation and wood-production trade-off.

Intensity of insect infestation in nut crops of black walnut varies inversely with crop size (Johnson 1969). This phenomenon occurs in orchards of all kinds where fruiting is sporadic. In pine seed orchards, mathematical analysis showed more precisely than previously known how insect-caused loss is related to variability in crop size (Mattson 1971). This analysis revealed that conditions which stabilize and increase seed production lead to greater insect-caused losses. At the same time, the interaction between fluctuating seed crops and insects suggests that manipulating crop size offers a potential means of regulating insects.

DEVELOPING WOOD CROPS

This is perhaps the most complex protection category because it involves a long growth period during which quality is very sensitive to cambial and wood injury by insects. As every log buyer knows, the quality of black walnut growing-stock inventory continues to dwindle. The most recent survey figures (Quigley and Lindmark 1967) show that only 15 percent of sawtimber volume is log grade 1, which includes veneer. Just how much insects contributed to this poor quality can only be guessed, but the present inventory represents growth essentially without protection from biotic agents. Baker (1972) discusses more than 50 kinds of insects that feed on forest black walnut. His treatise is useful but unstructured for black walnut wood production purposes.

Goal-setting speeds technological progress by molding and focusing problem-solving efforts. The black walnut wood production goal is instructive for protection purposes. The guiding product is the veneer log, which exceeds standards for log grade 1 (Freeman 1966) and is worth several times more money. Minimum dimensions of veneer logs are not standard, but many people might agree on 9 feet for length and 15 inches for top diameter. Such logs must be free of all defects, including insect holes (Clark 1969). The implications for protection are these: The first 9 to 17 feet of stem should grow uninterrupted and straight, the exact distance depending on length of log desired. This phase of height growth encompasses 5 to 10 years on most sites (Carmean 1970). After form-phase growth, annual radial increments should be maximized and maintained without blemishes to harvest. This incremental phase of growth encompasses 30 or more years (Clark 1969).

Form-Phase Insects

Insects in this group eat or otherwise injure terminals or elongating shoots. Apical dominance is tenuous in black walnut and disruptions are easily induced. When a leader bud or shoot dies, takeover by a lateral usually results in stem deformation. Shoot injuries of unclear origin, such as those mentioned by Moore (1967) and Ashworth (1969), are probably partly due to insects. More investigation will doubtless swell the following list of form-phase insects:

---

[2] *Personal correspondence with R. E. Phares, 1972. Data on file at the North Cent. For. Exp. Stn., St. Paul, Minn.*

1. Shoot moth (*Gwendolina concitatricana*). Only recently identified as a black walnut feeder, this insect occurs widely. In the only published report of its feeding, larvae killed 50 percent of the terminal buds of seedling sprouts in a Kansas stand (Naughton 1970). Its life cycle remains virtually unstudied. No regulation methods are known.

2. Case moths (*Acrobasis caryivorella* and *A. juglandis*). The larvae feed on buds, shoots, and leaves of black walnut and related trees. They build distinctive cases of silk and excrement. *Acrobasis caryivorella* produces from two to four generations a year (multivoltine) depending on latitude; *A. juglandis* is univoltine (Neunzig 1972). A related insect, *A. demotella*, feeds only on leaf petioles. Regulation measures based on pesticides have been developed for *A. caryivorella* (Phillips *et al.* 1964) and *A. juglandis* (Osburn *et al.* 1966) on pecan.

3. Curculio or weevil (*Conotrachelus retentus* and *C. juglandis*). Adults feed on terminals and leaf petioles before moving to nuts. Feeding signs are inconspicuous and may account for some unexplained deaths of buds. Adults lay eggs in some shoots, which are then mined by issuing larvae (Schoof 1942). Shoot infestations resemble frost injury (Renlund 1972).

4. Periodical cicadas (*Magicicada* spp.). Periodical cicadas include six allied species. Adults injure shoots and twigs by cutting egg niches. These heal slowly, kill some shoots, and increase breakage. In a given locality, periodical cicadas usually appear only at long intervals (17 or 13 years depending on latitude). Thus, form-phase black walnuts are not likely to be exposed more than once if at all. Small trees can be protected when cicadas appear by covering them with cloth, such as heavy cheesecloth or netting. Covers should remain in place for about 5 weeks. Cicadas can also be regulated with pesticides (U.S. Dep. Agric. 1971).

An accidentally imported ambrosia beetle, *Xylosandrus germanus*, was recently recovered in association with an unexplained dieback of black walnut saplings. Ambrosia beetles are normally nonaggressive feeders, but *Xylosandrus germanus* may not be typical (Heidenreich 1964). Its presence in two black walnut plantings in Indiana and Illinois represents two records; first occurrence on walnut and first appearance so far west (Bright 1968). Little is known about this Eurasian beetle in North America and it should be watched.

Although costly in labor and crop delay, shaping and coppicing are the best answers at present for insect-caused disruptions in form-phase growth. A practical guide for shaping is available (Krajicek and Bey 1969).

Increment-Phase Insects

This group comprises defoliators, sucking insects and mites, and borers. By the manner in which they affect wood production they can be subdivided into increment retarders and increment spoilers.

Increment retarders. — The most familiar insects of black walnut are in this subgroup. Heavy insect grazing on black walnut canopies may divert photosynthates and lessen biomass additions to stem and nut crops. The more important examples are:

1. Walnut caterpillar (*Datana integerrima*). This common leaf eater is uni- or multivoltine depending on latitude. Its tendency to late-season defoliation moderates its effect on trees. Major outbreaks are sporadic. Eggs are laid on leaves in the lower crown no higher than 18 feet from the ground. Larvae feed near eggs during the early part of their development. A nonchemical regulation measure is removing leaves or branches containing larvae or scorching them with a pole torch (Hixson 1941). Regulation by pesticides is also possible (Osburn *et al.* 1966). The pesticide-containing protective paint discussed by Shelton (1970) seems promising with long-lived pesticides but not short-lived ones.

2. Walnut aphids (*Monellia* spp. and others). Complex in life cycle, these insects suck sap and remove cell contents of leaves. Their sugary excretions, known as honeydew, build up on leaves, branches, stems, and ground beneath dense populations and support a sooty mold. Only chemical regulation measures are available (Johnson 1969). *Chromaphis juglandicola* was successfully regulated experimentally on Persian walnuts by injecting pesticide into trees (Heffernan 1967).

3. Spider mites (*Panonychus ulmi, Tetranychus urticae*, and others). These almost microscopic forms suck sap and remove cell contents of leaves. The above-named species are important in many kinds of crops. A grayish or bronze discoloration of leaves is a sign of dense and injurious populations. Only chemical regulation measures are available (Johnson 1969). More conspicuous but less damaging are microscopic nonspider mites of the eriophyid group. These cause leaf crinkling and velvety growths on leaves and shoots. The symptoms are well known (Johnson 1969), but mites I re-

covered from such growths in Illinois proved to be new to science.

4. Elm spanworm (*Ennomos subsignarius*). This widely distributed univoltine leaf eater feeds on a variety of trees but has a strong preference for black walnut. It can kill trees by persistent yearly defoliation. Only chemical regulation measures are available (Fedde 1971).

At least two dozen more insects could be mentioned (Baker 1972), and there may be some as yet undiscovered. There has been little search for insects feeding on black walnut roots, for example.

Increment-retarding insects exemplify the most pressing informational need concerning black walnut insects; namely, scientific evaluation of impact potential. By its long duration, increment-phase growth complicates insect regulation. One problem is assuring a return on protection investments. Ferell and Bentley (1969) considered economic aspects of black walnut wood production but they did not include insect-protection expenditures. Present levels of information about black walnut insects inadequately illuminate insect regulation alternatives.

Another complication is that trees can tolerate insect grazing on their leaves to an unknown degree without loss. Partial defoliation may not be detrimental because more light reaches leaves that normally would be shaded. Up to 50 percent removal of live crown caused no loss in stem increments in black walnut pruning experiments (Clark and Seidel 1961).

A more subtle complication is that cultural practices sometimes favor insect buildups. Stabilizing seed crops has already been mentioned as an example. Monoculture, in contrast to occasional individuals or small groups of black walnut in natural forests, is a cultural shift to which some insects will doubtless respond by increasing their numbers. Nitrogen fertilization appears to be promising in black walnut culture (Neely *et al.* 1970). Fertilizers and pesticides that are detrimental to some arthropods may stimulate others, notably sucking forms, by changing the physiological makeup of trees (Rodriguez 1960, Chaboussou 1965, and Stark 1965). The term trophobiosis was coined for such responses. Trophobiotic evidence comes from a wide range of crops, including at least one example from Persian walnut culture cited by Chaboussou (1965): the scale insect *Lecanium pruinosum* increased three- to more than tenfold following pesticide application.

Increment spoilers. — Insects in this group are borers. Typically, they infest trees that are stressed due to drought, defoliation, or other adverse factors. Black walnut is very sensitive to cambial disturbance; mechanical penetration may result in wounds much larger than the original hole (Clark 1966). Baker (1972) discusses more than 15 species of insects that bore in black walnut. The more aggressive forms are listed below:

1. Flatheaded apple tree borer (*Chrysobothris femorata*). Larvae of this normally univoltine beetle feed first beneath the bark and later bore into the wood. Trees can be protected by wrapping stems with high-grade wrapping paper or burlap (Fenton 1942). *Chrysobothris sexsignata* is a related species also occurring on black walnut.

2. American plum borer (*Euzophera semifuneralis*). Larvae of this moth bore in stems and large branches. No regulation measures are known.

3. White oak borer (*Goes tigrinus*). Larvae of this beetle occasionally infest black walnut, making holes up to 1 inch in diameter and 10 inches long. The life cycle requires 3 to 5 years depending on latitude. No regulation measures are known.

Two beetles that may belong in the list are *Agrilus otiosus* and *Pseudothysanoes lecontei*. Very little is known about them beyond occasional association with black walnut.

Certain woodpeckers are attracted to borer-infested black walnut trees (McAtee 1911). They may increase the size of the holes already present when they remove insects. The yellow-bellied sapsucker (*Sphyrapicus varius varius*) feeds on black walnut also (McAtee 1911). It causes most of the defect in black walnut known as birdpeck. The sapsucker actually feeds on sap and stem tissues. Although truly insectivorous as well, it catches free-living insects rather than those boring in wood (Rushmore 1969).

Tree stress cannot now be gauged meaningfully enough for efficient application of borer regulation measures like stem wrapping. The broad correlation between borer infestation and tree stress suggests that irrigation during drought is a potential borer regulation measure.

ACTION AT COMMUNITY LEVEL

In contrast to insect regulation measures that one owner may apply in one planting, some types of actions benefit the broad community of owners and plantings. Border quarantine and research are notable examples; the relevance of three others to black walnut are briefly discussed below.

Tree improvement. — Named varieties of black walnut as well as tree improvement research reveal that traits important for nut and wood production vary genetically. Certain strains of black and Persian walnuts mature late, a trait that desynchronizes husk and husk fly development to the detriment of the insect (Johnson 1969, Somers 1968). Inherent susceptibility of black walnut to other insects might likewise vary. Too little is now known about black walnut insects for tree improvement purposes, however. As a result, feeding patterns by different insects in early performance studies of black walnut selections have been uninstructively lumped (Bey 1970).

Biological insect regulation. — On Persian walnut in California, early results show promise for community-wide regulation of the aphid *Chromaphis juglandicola* with the imported parasitic wasp *Trioxyus pallidus* (Van den Bosch *et al.* 1962). An installation for research in biological regulation of insects has been established by the USDA Agricultural Research Service at Columbia, Missouri. An opportunity also exists for exploring biological regulation of black walnut insects under foreign agricultural research provisions of Public Law 480 (Fowells 1970). For example, at least a dozen kinds of walnut insects are known in Himalayan Asia (Browne 1968, Janjua and Chaudhry 1964). Under Public Law 480, their parasites and predators could be searched out and evaluated for importation.

Insect reporting services. — Seasonal insect development, local insect movements or buildups, and other early warning information could be useful in walnut protection. In Illinois, the *Insect, Weed, and Plant Disease Survey Bulletin* is issued weekly from the latter part of March to August by the University of Illinois. Many other States assemble and distribute such information also.

CONCLUSION

Some information has accumulated about insects as related to black walnut wood and nut production. New knowledge about insects is not keeping pace with progress in other aspects of black walnut production technology. Insect management cannot be developed in isolation because insects interact with other production factors. The most immediate need is rigorous impact evaluation of known insects and closer scrutiny of developing crops for overlooked losses due to insects.

LITERATURE CITED

Ashworth, F. L. 1969. Tip bud dominance in black walnut seedlings North. Nut Grow. Assoc. Annu. Rep. 60: 74.

Baker, W. L. 1972. Eastern forest insects. USDA For. Serv. Misc. Publ. 1175, 642 p.

Barcia, D. R., and E. P. Merkel. 1972. Bibliography on insects destructive to flowers, cones, and seeds of North American conifers. USDA For. Serv. Res. Pap. SE-92, 80 p. Southeast. For. Exp Stn., Asheville, N. C.

Bey, C. F. 1970. Geographic variation for seed and seedling characters in black walnut. USDA For. Serv. Res. Note NC-101, 4 p. North Cent. For. Exp. Stn., St. Paul, Minn.

Bright, D. E. 1968. Review of the tribe Xyleborini in America north of Mexico (Coleoptera: Scolytidae). Can. Entomol. 100: 1288-1323.

Browne, F. G. 1968. Pests and diseases of forest plantation trees. 1330 p. Oxford: Clarendon Press.

Carmean, W. H. 1970. Tree height-growth patterns in relation to soil and site. *In* Tree growth and forest soils, C. T. Youngberg and C. B. Davey, eds. p. 499-512. Third North Am. For. Soils Conf. Proc.

Chaboussou, F. 1965. Nouveaux aspects de la phytiatrie et de la phytopharmacie. Le phenomene de la trophobiose. FAO Symp. Integrated Pest Control Proc. 1: 33-61.

Clark, F. B. 1966. Increment borers cause serious degrade in black walnut. J. For. 64: 814.

Clark, F. B. 1969. Growing black walnut timber. *In* Handbook of North American nut trees, R. A. Jaynes, ed. p. 212-223. North. Nut Grow. Assoc. 421 p.

Clark, F. B., and K. W. Seidel. 1961. Growth and quality of pruned black walnut. USDA For. Serv., Cent. States For. Exp. Stn. Tech. Pap. 180, 11 p.

Fedde, G. F. 1971. Elm spanworm. USDA For. Serv. For. Pest Leafl. 81, 6 p.

Fenton, F. A. 1942. The flatheaded apple tree borer (*Chrysobothris femorata* (Olivier)). Okla. Agric. Exp. Stn. Bull. B-259, 31 p.

Ferell, R. S., and W. R. Bentley. 1969. Plantation investment opportunities in black walnut. J. For. 67: 250-254.

Fowells, H. A. 1970. Science and a hungry world. J. Wash. Acad. Sci. 60: 88-92.

Freeman, E. E. 1966. Quality requirements for saw logs. *In* Black walnut culture. p. 68-71. USDA For. Serv., North Cent. For. Exp. Stn., 94 p.

Harcourt, D. G. 1970. Crop life tables as a pest management tool. Can. Entomol. 102: 950-955.

Hay, C. J., and D. E. Donley. 1966. Insect pests. *In* Black walnut culture. p. 83-87. USDA For. Serv., North Cent. For. Exp. Stn., 94 p.

Heffernan, T. 1967. Oxydemetonmethyl implanted to English walnuts for control of walnut aphid. J. Econ. Entomol. 60: 890-891.

Heidenreich, E. 1964. Oekologische Bedingungen fuer Primaerbefall durch "*Xylosandrus germanus*." Z. angew. Entomol. 54: 131-140.

Hixson, E. 1941. The walnut Datana. Okla. Agric. Exp. Sta. Bull. B-246, 29 p.

Janjua, N. A., and G. U. Chaudhry. 1964. Biology and control of hill fruit insects of West Pakistan. Food and Agric. Counc., Ministry of Agric., Gov. of Pakistan, 158 p.

Johnson, W. T. 1969. Plant pests. *In* Handbook of North American nut trees, R. A. Jaynes, ed. p. 67-156. North. Nut Grow. Assoc. 421 p.

Krajicek, J. E., and C. F. Bey. 1969. How to "train" black walnut seedlings. USDA For. Serv., North Cent. For. Exp. Stn., unpaged pamphlet.

McAtee, W. L. 1911. Woodpeckers in relation to trees and wood products. U.S. Dep. Agric. Biol. Surv. Bull. 39, 99 p.

Matthews, J. D. 1963. Factors affecting the production of seed by forest trees. For. Abstr. 24: 1-13.

Mattson, W. J. 1971. Relationship between cone crop size and cone damage by insects in red pine seed-production areas. Can. Entomol. 103: 617-621.

Michelbacher, A. E., and J. C. Ortega. 1958. A technical study of insects and related pests attacking walnuts. Calif. Agric. Exp. Stn. Bull. 764, 86 p.

Moore, J. 1967. Growing black walnut for timber. North. Nut Grow. Assoc. Annu. Rep. 58: 128-133.

Naughton, G. G. 1970. Black walnut deformed by shoot moth. J. For. 68: 28-29.

Neely, D., E. B. Himelick, and W. R. Crowley. 1970. Fertilization of established trees: a report of field studies. Ill. Nat. Hist. Surv. Bull. 30(4): 235-266.

Neunzig, H. H. 1972. Taxonomy of *Acrobasis* larvae and pupae in eastern North America (Lepidoptera: Pyralidae). U.S. Dep. Agric. Tech. Bull. 1457, 158 p.

Nickel, J. L., and T. Y. Wong. 1966. Control of the walnut husk fly, *Rhagoletis completa* Cresson, with systemic insecticides. J. Econ. Entomol. 59: 1079-1082.

Osburn, M. R., W. C. Pierce, A. M. Phillips, J. R. Cole, and G. E. Ken-Knight. 1966. Controlling insects and diseases of the pecan. U.S. Dep. Agric., Agric. Handb. 240, 55 p.

Phillips, A. M., J. R. Large, and J. R. Cole. 1964. Insects and diseases of the pecan in Florida. Fla. Agric. Exp. Stn. Bull. 619A, 87 p.

Quigley, K. L., and R. D. Lindmark. 1967. A look at black walnut timber resources and industries. USDA For. Serv. Resour. Bull. NE-4, 28 p. Northeast. For. Exp. Stn., Upper Darby, Pa.

Renlund, D. W. 1972. Wisconsin forest pest situation report, 1972. Wis. Dep. Nat. Resour., 9 p.

Rodriguez, J. G. 1960. Nutrition of the host and reaction to pests. *In* Biological and chemical control of plant and animal pests, L. P. Reitz, ed. p. 149-167. Am. Assoc. Adv. Sci. Publ. 61, 273 p.

Rushmore, F. M. 1969. Sapsucker damage varies with tree species and seasons. USDA For. Serv. Res. Pap. NE-136, 19 p. Northeast. For. Exp. Stn., Upper Darby, Pa.

Schneider, G. 1970. Biomass and macro-nutrient content in a 31-year-old black walnut plantation. Mich. Acad. 2(4): 33-42.

Schoof, H. F. 1942. The genus *Conotrachelus* Dejean (Coleoptera, Curculionidae) in the North Central United States. Ill. Biol. Monogr. 14(3), 170 p.

Shelton, E. M. 1970. A protective paint for tree trunks. North. Nut Grow. Assoc. Annu. Rep. 61: 43-44.

Somers, L. 1968. Some experiences in the control of Carpathian walnut insect pests. North. Nut Grow. Assoc. Annu. Rep. 59: 80-81.

Stark, R. W. 1965. Recent trends in forest entomology. Annu. Rev. Entomol. 10: 303-324.

U.S. Department of Agriculture. 1971. Periodical cicadas. U.S. Dep. Agric. Leafl. 540, 8 p.

Van den Bosch, R., E. I. Schlinger, and K. S. Hagen. 1962. Initial field observations in California on *Trioxys pallidus* (Haliday), a recently introduced parasite of the walnut aphid. J. Econ. Entomol. 55: 857-862.

Wylie, J. E. 1966. Nuts and wood — dual crops for management. *In* Black walnut culture. p. 91-94. USDA For. Serv., North Cent. For. Exp. Stn. 94 p.

EVALUATING ECONOMIC MATURITY
OF INDIVIDUAL TREES

Gary G. Naughton, *Assistant State Forester*
Kansas State University
Manhattan, Kansas

ABSTRACT.—The descision to cut a walnut tree should be carefully weighed in terms of its present value as opposed to its future value. Maximum economic yield is possible when each tree is evaluated as an individual in terms of its own quality, size, and growth rate. Instructions are given for the use of a graph to find the compound earning rate and examples show the effects of pruning and release.

Because of prevailing high stumpage prices for black walnut logs and veneer bolts, landowners are frequently faced with the question of whether to cut a particular tree now or allow it to continue to grow.

Foresters, in giving marketing advice to landowners in these situations, can usually spot individual trees which they know — by experience — should be cut or left on the basis of their apparent present value compared to their value as a "growing" investment. However, some of the thoughts which are behind these decisions on economic maturity are not easily explained. Economic decision processes provide an excellent way of showing the potential rate of return of individual trees.

The intent of this paper is to present a simple means of predicting future return for individual trees in relation to present size and rate of growth, using current average stumpage prices. The Doyle log rule was used for all volume calculations.

Stumpage values are principally influenced by tree location, quality, size, and mill price. If we assume that tree location and mill price are factors that the owner cannot change, then the only things the owner can do to increase his total return from a tree are those related to its quality and size at market time.

Reducing stand density and pruning greatly influence tree growth rate and quality. If a tree can be improved in grade or accelerated in growth, it increases in future market value.

Although dollar values are not the only factors to consider in deciding whether to cut a tree, it is desirable to consider the future economic potential of a tree because it is a *measurable* factor for guiding the decision. Growth in value is influenced by the rate of volume growth and the premium price placed on large diameter logs. When the owner knows the minimum rate of return he is willing to accept, he has established his economic alternative rate — the point below which he will cut a particular tree and re-invest proceeds. He can predict the present earning (compound) rate for each tree evaluated (fig. 1).

FINDING THE COMPOUND EARNING RATE

The compound earning rate is the annual rate of value increase over a period of years. To find the compound earning rate using figure 1:

1. First measure the tree d.b.h. (diameter breast high) to the nearest $1/10$ inch.

2. Determine the grade of the butt log — prime, select, or common, according to the following definitions:

Prime. — Sound, straight, free of all defects.

Select. — Must have three clear (prime) faces; slight crook permitted if otherwise prime.

Common. — All logs (except cull) which are not select or higher.

3. Estimate the rate of growth as slow, medium, or fast according to the following definitions:

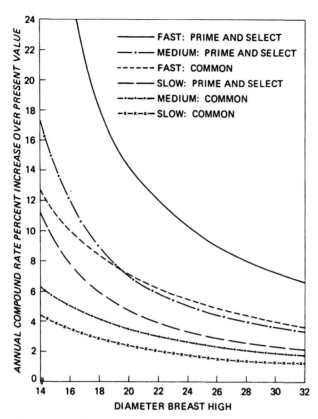

Figure 1. — *Spot evaluation of walnut trees — a guide for determining economic maturity of individual trees, F.C. 80 assumed. Plotted curves are at growth rate of: 4 rings per inch = fast; 8 rings per inch = medium; 12 rings per inch = slow.*

Fast. — Less than six rings per inch.

Medium. — Six to ten rings per inch.

Slow. — More than 10 rings per inch.

On the basis of site, growing space, and bark and crown characteristics, experienced foresters can place a tree in one of these three categories without the necessity of making increment borings. The landowner's personal knowledge of tree ages and growth rates can be used also.

4. Go to the bottom of figure 1 and find d.b.h.

5. Follow vertical d.b.h. line until it intersects with the proper growth and grade curve.

6. Follow horizontal line nearest this intersection to the vertical axis on the left to read off the compound earning rate.

Points to Remember

1. The graph shows only relative compound earning rates on basis of present value — not value in dollars.

2. Earning *rates* for select logs and prime logs are generally the same at any given d.b.h. and growth rate, because the stumpage values of select logs are a fixed percentage of the prime rate.

3. Whereas prime and select log prices go up in value per board foot with increased size, common log prices per foot are relatively fixed at *all* sizes.

4. Although 16-foot logs were used in the basic calculations, *relative earning rate* per log does not change appreciably as length is dropped to 12 feet, 10 feet, or 8 feet — only total value per log is affected.

5. Future changes in market prices (per board foot) will have no effect on the accuracy of these rate curves unless the relationship of value to log size and quality changes appreciably. Pricing factors that favor larger sizes and higher grades are built in.

6. Do not use this system on "high risk" trees or any other individuals where the decision to "cut or keep" can be made on some other appropriate basis. "High risk" trees are those that might not survive in the stand until the next harvest cut because of existing hazards.

7. Rates of return on "common" grades are applicable to *any* species sold on the Doyle Rule which does not have a premium price per unit on the basis of size or quality.

8. The rates of return were computed from tables listing values $(1 + i)^n$ in tenths of a percent using the formula:

$$\frac{V_n}{V_o} = (1 + i)^n;$$

where V_n = value in n years
V_o = value now
i = compound rate
n = years required per inch
of d.b.h. growth

9. *Average* stumpage value for walnut trees can be computed by the following formula: Find a base minimum price for prime logs (30¢ per board foot in this

example). For each inch of log diameter above the minimum (12 inches in this example), add 5¢ per board foot.

Prime per board foot = 30¢ + 5 (d.i.b.-12); thus, a tree with the d.i.b.
(diameter inside bark at small end)
of 18 inches would be
30¢ + 5(18 - 12) = 30¢ + 5(6) =

30¢ + 30¢ = 60¢ per board foot.

Select = ½ the value of prime logs of the identical size.

Common per board foot = variable from 8¢ to 10¢ per board foot. There is no significant premium for common grade logs in larger diameter.

(Note: Market prices vary locally and seasonally, but tend to follow a pattern similar to that shown. The point here is to show the relative value.)

Effects of Pruning and Release

Volume is affected by both the length *and* the diameter of the log. Increasing the d.i.b. without increasing the length of the log gives us a much slower *rate* of volume increase (fig. 2). Remember that diameter and length increases are both important and that clear length may be added by pruning the tree higher. Thus, pruning at the proper time can add significantly to total value of a particular tree. Using the stumpage values given earlier, a 16-inch log (prime grade) is worth: $36 if 8 feet long, $45 if 10 feet long, $54 if 12 feet long.

It is obvious that, if it costs $1 to prune a tree to the minimum 8-foot log, this dollar has the greatest rate of return if the log would have otherwise been common grade worth $7.20. Value gained on the second and third prunings is much less significant but still worth the cost. The value as related to the cost of thinning and weeding can be estimated by use of the growth rate-earning rate curves. Release of pole-sized walnut from competition has yielded some rather dramatic increases in diameter growth rate.

EXAMPLE

A good quality walnut tree — potential prime log — 14 inches in d.b.h. — is found in a crowded young stand

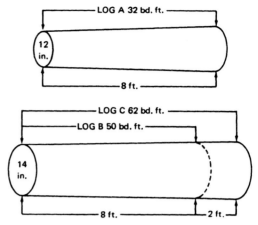

Log B volume increases 56 percent over Log A.
Log C volume increases 94 percent over Log A.

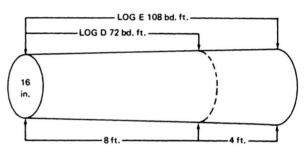

Log D volume increases 44 percent over Log B.
Log E volume increases 74 percent over Log C.

Figure 2. — *Schematic diagram to show how a 2-foot increase in log length together with a 2-inch increase in d.i.b. boosts volume considerably more than a 2-inch increase in d.i.b. alone.*

of boxelder and ash. Current growth rate is eight rings per inch of diameter. After the tree is released from competition by clearing a 16-foot radius around the stem, it will accelerate to an average growth rate of four rings per inch. The rate of value increase per year jumps from 17 percent to over 24 percent (off the chart) (fig. 1).

If it costs $5 to release the tree from competition, and the management objective is a 22-inch-d.b.h. by 16-foot veneer log: At eight rings per inch it would take 32 more years to bring the tree to market size. At four rings per inch it would take 18 more years (allowing 2 years for gradual growth response).

The potential market value is the same in either case, 196 board feet x 60¢ = $117.60. This $117.60 future sale value is worth less today than at the day of sale because of the discounted value of a future income — a reverse compound interest — comparable to what money you would have to put in the bank now to have $117.60 at some future time.

If it costs you 6 percent interest to borrow money, then you must compute your investment rate at 6 percent. Thus:

$117.60 discounted 18 years at 6 percent becomes

$$X = \frac{117.60}{(1 + .06)^{18}} = \frac{117.60}{2.85434} = \$41.20$$

now for the fast growing tree

but,

$117.60 discounted 32 years at 6 percent becomes

$$X = \frac{117.60}{(1 + .06)^{32}} = \frac{117.60}{6.45339} = \$18.22$$

now for the slower growing tree.

The difference here of $22.98 present value is the result of spending $5 now to give the tree more growing space. The $5 must be deducted from the $22.98 gain shown, but still leaves a net gain of $17.98 per tree treated in this way. If you had several such trees on 1 acre, the results could be spectacular.

COST AND INCOME TREATMENT
ON SMALL WOODLANDS

Steven E. Lindsey, *Area Extension Forester*
Kansas State and Extension Forestry, Kansas State University
Hutchinson, Kansas

ABSTRACT.—Universal demand and high value commonly associated with the sale of walnut timber may result in an excessive tax burden to farmer/woodland owners. It is the purpose of this report to present the proper treatment of incurred costs and the use, benefits, and regulations of long-term capital gains and losses as related to the small individual timber owner.

The sale of walnut timber, because of its universal demand and premium price, can result in an excessive tax burden to the small woodland owner if not handled properly. Quite often the sale of only a few large, high-quality trees can severely upset the farmer/woodland owner's estimated tax return. Unless the owner is familiar with the use, regulations, and benefits of long-term capital gain treatment of timber investments and the proper treatment of incurred costs, he may well forfeit his right to these benefits and pay more tax on the sale or harvest of timber than is legally due.

The sale of walnut timber is usually an infrequent event for the individual small woodland owner. Yet, a considerable volume of walnut timber is sold and harvested annually from such ownerships. Several hundred acres of black walnut plantations are established annually on small holdings. It is the purpose of this report to outline the treatment of costs incurred on small woodlands, and to interpret the regulations governing the treatment of forest income as long-term capital gain and loss. It is not necessarily within the scope of this report to cover all treatments for individual cases, but rather to interpret the tax regulations to guide the farmer/woodland owner in financial arrangements and decisions in managing costs and returns on the small woodland.

Although this report is primarily concerned with growing and harvesting walnut timber, its content in most cases may be applied to other timber crops.

COST TREATMENT

Before dealing with forest income, the woodland owner should be acquainted with the treatment of necessary costs incurred while managing the timber crop. Most costs can be classified beneath the general headings of depletion, capital expenditures, and operating costs.

Depletion

The investment cost of timber is recovered at the time of harvest through a tax deduction called "depletion." This deduction (depletion allowance) is determined by multiplying the volume of timber cut during the taxable year by the appropriate depletion rate. This rate is determined by dividing the total cruised volume immediately prior to harvest into the initial cost of the timber plus other proper additions to the investment cost (original cost and subsequent capitalized improvements) for the first sale. For all subsequent sales, the depletion rate is such that total depletion allowed to the remaining merchantable timber is equal to the remaining cost.

Example

An owner bought a farm in 1950 for $20,000; the farm supported 160,000 board feet of standing timber valued at $2,000. In 1965, the same owner sold outright 50,000 board feet of timber for $20 per thousand board feet, or $1,000. By the date of sale, the stand had increased 40,000 board feet due to growth, totaling 200,000 board feet. The depletion rate was found to be $10 per thousand, or $500, indicating a gain of $500.

Original purchase	160 M bd. ft. at $2,000	
Growth	+ 40 M bd. ft.	
Depletion basis		2,000
Total timber available for cutting	200 M bd. ft.	
Depletion rate ($2,000 ÷ 200 M bd.ft.)=		10
Depletion allowance ($10 x 50 M bd. ft.) =		500
Total proceeds from sale		1,000
Less depletion allowance		– 500
Gain from sale		500
Depletion basis for future sales ($2,000 less $500) =		1,500

The depletion allowance is never computed from replacement cost, but rather from the investment cost. Depletion is formulated to recover capital investment costs of timber only; separate of land, physical plants, and equipment, though all were purchased in one unit. Therefore, when a tract of land supporting merchantable timber is purchased, it must be inventoried to establish the initial market value of the timber only, which is the investment cost of the timber. Gross income is reduced by the depletion allowance whether the income from timber harvests is fully taxed as ordinary income or taxed at a reduced rate under the provisions of capital gain and loss treatment. The depletion basis will need to be increased by the allocated value of additional timber purchases and by the amount of capitalized expenditures. Adjustments must also be made to reflect timber sales, casualty losses, and growth.

In the event that no depletion basis was established at the time timberland was purchased, that portion of the property which should have been allocated to timber will need to be known. If the purchase was cutover land or land supporting only immature timber, there will usually be no original depletion basis. If merchantable timber was present at the time of purchase, a forester should be consulted to establish its volume and fair market value. This information will establish the original depletion basis.

Capital Expenditures

The treatment of incurred costs in growing plantation walnut or managing native walnut is sometimes a problem to the small farmer/woodland owner. Some expenditures must be capitalized while others must be expensed. Capitalized expenditures cannot be deducted in the year incurred, but recovered through depletion or depreciation. Expensed costs may be deducted in the year incurred. It would be impractical to place all items of possible expenditure into a particular category, but some general guidelines can be drawn.

The Internal Revenue Service defines capital expenditures as "the amount paid or debt incurred for the acquisition, improvement, or restoration of an asset having a useful life of more than one year." These expenditures cannot be expensed, but may be recovered through depletion and/or depreciation allowances.

When land is purchased, the total purchase price (including costs for appraisal, land survey, recording fees, abstract search, and legal services) must be allocated to either timber, land, or buildings. This allocation must be proportional to the fair market values of each as of the date of purchase. From this allocation comes the investment cost of merchantable timber, which is only recoverable by depletion allowance at the time of sale or harvest. If no separate timber valuation was established when the farm or woodland was purchased, the proportional amount should be established. If no merchantable timber was on the property at the time of purchase, no allocation can be established for depletion.

The costs incurred in establishing a walnut plantation are considered to be capital expenditures. Site preparation for seeding and planting, cost of seed and seedlings, and the cost of labor to plant or seed are all to be capitalized. These expenditures are considered to be the investment cost of the timber, and thus are only recoverable through depletion allowance at sale or harvest. Other costs which should be capitalized are fences, fertilizers, roads, bridges, firebreaks, and the cost of equipment with a useful life of more than 1 year.

Operating Expenses

Operating expenses can be expensed. These expenditures are deductible from gross income as costs incurred during the taxable year as related to the production of income from timber stands. The individual farmer/woodland owner may expense ordinary and necessary expenses for the management, conservation, and maintenance of property held for the production of income. These costs include weed control, pruning and thinning of immature timber, cultivation, understory brush control, short-life tools and minor equipment repairs, normal labor (excluding labor required to be capitalized), cutting and processing, materials and supplies, temporary roads, consulting fees, and other management costs. Deductible expenses are usually limited to costs for improvements having a useful life of less than one growing season. If the useful life of improvements cannot be determined, then these costs should be capitalized and recovered by depletion at the time of sale or harvest. If the useful life of such improvements is determinable for more than 1 year, the costs may be recovered through annual allowances for depreciation.

If the plantation or timber is in a preproductive stage, the land owner has the option of either expensing or capitalizing most normal operating expenses. This option would normally apply to taxes, interest, maintenance, fertilizer, controlling undergrowth, and cultivating and spraying trees. This option is mentioned as one method of treating costs incurred early in plantation establishment, though the individual farmer/woodland owner would seldom capitalize such expenses.

Depreciation

The cost of property (tools, equipment, buildings, etc.) used in the trade or business or held for the production of income may not be expensed in the year of purchase. However, the owner is allowed to "deduct a reasonable allowance for the exhaustion, wear and tear, and obsolescence of such property as depreciation." The depreciation deduction, not unlike the depletion allowance, is never determined from replacement cost. Though several different methods are used in figuring depreciation, the basic concept is to allow annual deductions proportional to the life expectancy of the property with reference to its original cost.

CAPITAL GAINS AND LOSSES

The Federal Internal Revenue Code provides for special tax treatment of gains and losses from sales or exchanges of capital assets. Such long-term capital gains or losses (assets held more than 6 months) are reduced by 50 percent before being taxed; and if total capital gains are less than $50,000 (Tax Reform Act of 1969), the tax is further limited to a maximum of 25 percent of the long-term capital gain.

The maximum rate of 25 percent as interpreted in the Tax Reform Act of 1969 is available to individuals for only the first $50,000. Tax on the net long-term capital gain in excess of $50,000 results in a maximum of 35 percent.

Capital gains and losses are given even more favored tax treatment in that the net long-term capital loss is deductible to the extent of the lesser of: (1) $1,000, (2) the taxable income of the current year, figured without including capital gains or losses and without including personal exemptions, or (3) the excess of net short-term capital loss over the net long-term capital gain plus 50 percent of the excess net long-term capital loss over the net short-term capital gain. "Any capital loss not used in the current year because of the above limitation is permitted to be carried over to succeeding years."

Congress, in its attempt to promote continuous forest management, did apply certain basic ground rules in order for timber transactions to qualify for capital gains and losses — the timber or the cutting right to timber must in all cases be held in ownership more than 6 months *prior to* the beginning of the taxable year of sale. This requirement met, there are basically three approaches that may entitle the use of long-term capital gains treatment of woodland income: (1) infrequent transactions, (2) retained economic interest, and (3) cutting one's own timber to treat as a sale.

Infrequent Sales

Whether infrequent sales qualify for ordinary or capital gain and loss treatment depends upon whether the timber is considered to be a capital asset. Commonly, if sales are so occasional as to be considered infrequent, and are unrelated to a trade or business in which the owner is engaged (not necessarily owner's principle occupation), the timber will qualify for treatment as a capital asset. The sale may include all timber, one or more species, or marked timber, but does not necessarily mean the liquidation of all timber. Timber sold must be sold for a lump sum. It must be sold outright, payment being a fixed amount agreed upon in advance. The important criterion here is that the woodland owner can sell his timber to a buyer and expect capital gains treatment unless the sale is "in the ordinary course of his trade or business."

Capital gains and losses resulting from infrequent, lump-sum sales are reported on Schedule D (Form 1040), Department of Treasury, Internal Revenue Service.

Retained Economic Interest

Whatever problems are involved in applying capital gains treatment to the outright lump-sum sale are easily overcome by following the guides to transactions where economic interest is retained by the owner. Economic interest is usually retained where the owner is to be paid: (1) so much per cord, thousand board feet, or other convenient unit as stumpage is cut (pay-as-cut), (2) out of the production from stumpage disposed of, or (3) out of gross proceeds of sale of stumpage by the contractor.

When timber is sold where an economic interest is retained, ownership of the timber is retained until the trees are in fact cut by the purchaser. Title of the timber does not change hands until the tree is severed from its roots. The main criterion here is that the timber owner must rely upon the volume of timber cut to determine the compensation he will receive.

Two important advantages are apparent when timber is sold by contract with an economic interest retained. The Internal Revenue Service provides that timber is considered to be property in trade or business regardless of whether such timber is held primarily for sale to customers in the ordinary course of the owner's business. And, this type of sale also gives the owner more control over the timber sale.

Reporting gain or loss from the disposal of timber under these provisions facilitates paperwork in reporting taxes. Gains and losses are reported on Form 4797, Department of Treasury, Internal Revenue Service, along with other gains and losses the farmer may have sustained during the taxable year. The gain from the sale of timber is simply the difference between the gross sale price and the sum of depletion and other costs. Taxable gains and losses are then grouped with other sales, exchanges, or disposition of property held more than 6 months prior to the beginning of the taxable year that are a part of the normal farming business.

Cutting One's Own Timber

If the farmer/woodland owner elects to treat the gain from timber he cuts as capital gains and losses (usually his advantage to do so), he must separate the value of the standing timber from the sale proceeds of resulting products. Capital gains are figured from the value of standing trees only; product price minus labor and transportation equals market value of standing timber.

This section of the Revenue Code applies to the timber owner who cuts his own timber for sale or for use in his business or trade.

Gain or loss from stumpage is computed as the difference between the fair market value on the first day of the taxable year and the depletion basis of the standing timber. This transaction may be treated as long-term capital gain or loss. The difference between the fair market value of the timber and the proceeds from the sale of resulting products, less costs, is in all cases treated as ordinary income.

If the timber owner elects to treat the timber he cuts for sale or use in his business, he must do so in subsequent years. Once the method is elected, it must be continued unless undue hardship can be shown and permission is obtained from the Internal Revenue Service to discontinue it.

The fair market value in this section must be established by the timber owner to the satisfaction of the Internal Revenue Service. The fair market value is considered to be the owner's cost in timber or the stumpage cost in a hypothetical sale by the owner to himself. Assistance in establishing this figure can be obtained upon request from the local extension, consulting, or farm forester.

In reporting gains and losses from this treatment, capital gains and losses are reported on Form 4797, which is similar to reporting income from contract sales where an economic interest was retained. The income from the sale of logs or converted products is treated as ordinary income. Farmers should report this gain on Form 1040, Schedule F, as other farm income. These gains would be reported on Schedule C by individual woodland owners, other than farmers.

Other Sales and Receipts

Payment received from forest products other than standing timber is treated as ordinary income. Logs, lumber, gunstock blanks, fenceposts, firewood, chips, nuts, and bark are all reported as ordinary income. Income from such products would, in the case of the farmer, be reported on Schedule F, Form 1040. Similar receipts would be reported on Schedule C, Form 1040, for owners other than farmers.

Government payments for approved conservation programs must be included as gross income, whether received in cash, materials, or services. The gross cost-sharing payment, actively or constructively received, is reported on Schedule F, Form 1040. Since these payments are included as income, the expenditures for which payment was received must be treated as though no program was available. Total tree planting costs would continue to be capitalized and recovered through depletion at the time of sale or harvest.

Casualties and condemnations which may result in gains must be included as income. These gains, if held for more than 6 months and are considered capital assets, are reported on Part I, Form 4797, and treated as long-term capital gains. If the timber was not held for 6 months, it is reported in Part II, Form 4797.

Casualty, theft, and condemnation may in fact show a loss. In such cases, the loss may not exceed the depletion basis of the timber minus any salvage, insurance, or other compensations.

RETURNS FROM TWO SYSTEMS OF MULTICROPPING

Richard C. Smith, *Professor of Forestry*
University of Missouri
Columbia, Missouri

ABSTRACT.—An analysis was made of costs and returns from two hypothetical black walnut plantations of different spacings in which fescue was grown for seed between the rows of trees and nuts were sold. Fescue seed and nuts contributed a substantial share to total revenue. After allowance for all costs including income taxes, the internal rates of return were 8.3 and 12.9 percent respectively for the 18- by 18- and 40- by 40-foot spacings. Benefit-cost ratios were 1.39 and 1.67, based on a 6 percent discount rate. With the cost of land and initial costs of establishment assumed, $15,000 to $16,000 would be required to start a 40-acre plantation.

Interest in planting black walnut in Missouri is high — particularly because of the concepts of multiple cropping and the growing of superior trees from selected planting stock. Black walnut is unusual because substantial annual returns from nut harvests are possible at a relatively early age.

Genetically improved planting stock generally is not available, but at least a few investors have upgraded available nursery stock by using only the largest and most vigorous seedlings. If trees can be selected for desirable nut characteristics, such as large size and quality of nutmeat, annual revenues can be increased; rapidly growing trees can shorten the period to produce high-grade veneer logs.

Opportunities are being explored to grow agricultural crops, such as hay, orchard grass, or fescue for seed between rows of planted walnut trees. Cattle grazing appears promising if walnut trees can be protected from browsing and trampling. Agricultural crops and nut harvest bring early revenue to offset the initial cost of tree establishment.

What are the costs and returns from multiple cropping of black walnut? How much does the sale of nuts and other crops contribute to total returns? Is multiple cropping attractive as an investment? Plantations old enough to help quantify answers to such questions are not known. To explore multiple cropping investments, two hypothetical black walnut plantations were analyzed to provide an estimate of profitability. The data used are admittedly incomplete and somewhat speculative but are the best available.

STAND DEVELOPMENT

For both alternatives, a 40-acre plantation was assumed, but the analysis was made for a unit of 1 acre. Land was purchased at a cost of $200 per acre, including the amount paid and all costs of acquisition. If land were already owned, this amount would represent the opportunity cost of removing the land from other productive use. Part of the area, it was assumed, required clearing and terracing and the entire field was plowed and disced. Fertilizer was applied to eliminate nutrient deficiencies for fescue as indicated by soil testing. Because the enterprise was considered to be part of a farm operation, a fence was installed on the exterior boundary to exclude livestock. The area was seeded to fescue in the fall and walnut trees were planted the following spring. Subsequently, fescue was eliminated from around each seedling by use of an herbicide. Elimination of competing vegetation was continued in the second and third years as recommended by Krajicek and Williams (1971).

Production of annual crops of fescue seed continued. Walnut trees were pruned in three stages to form clear stems, once at age 10 and again at ages 15 and 20.

For Case A it was assumed that walnut seedlings were planted at a spacing of 18 by 18 feet, 135 trees per acre. This spacing is relatively open compared to that used for conventional timber production. However, the rows of trees were sufficiently close to reduce the yield of fescue, and the efficiency of combining and other equipment would be less than desired. Consequently, the fescue seed yield was assumed to be one-half that when grown under more open conditions.

The timber stand was managed in a traditional manner, with thinnings made at 5-year intervals, beginning at age 25. The volume removed varied from about 500 to 1,000 board feet (table 1). At age 80 the stand contained 7,100 board feet per acre and was harvested.

Nut production began at age 15 with 400 pounds per acre. The quantity harvested increased until age 35, then began to decline because the effect of tree removal by thinning more than offset increasing nut yield per tree. Nut yields were based on data derived from Naughton (1970). Although nut yields are shown as a uniform progression from year to year, it is recognized that actual nut yields may vary widely in an erratic manner. At least, the reasons are not apparent from examination of yield data.

Case B differs from Case A primarily because only 26 seedlings were planted per acre at a spacing of 40 by 40 feet and no thinning was necessary. A 40-foot strip at the edges of the field facilitated operation of farm equipment through the 80-year production period. Wider tree spacing permitted a larger area for growing fescue so yields were double those for Case A. Because the trees in Case B are open-grown, nut yields were increased by 10 percent.

By age 80 the 26 trees, four more trees than for Case A, contained 8,400 board feet.

COSTS

The cost of land was $200 per acre. For a 40-acre field, 1 mile of fence was required. Recently constructed fences in central Missouri have cost $1,800 to $2,000 per mile; the $2,000 rate was used. Initial costs for stand establishment were based on records for the Roubidoux Walnut Plantation, established in 1968 on the Clark National Forest. To provide for rising cost levels and greater precision required for this type of plantation, costs were doubled. The initial costs per acre for each walnut plantation are summarized:

	Case A	Case B
Land	$200.00	$200.00
Fertilizer	75.00	75.00
Fencing	50.00	50.00
Clearing and Site preparation	26.00	26.00
Planting stock	13.50	2.60
Sorting and trimming planting stock	4.10	0.80
Labor, supervision, transportation	16.75	11.30
Vegetation control, chemical and labor	5.40	1.05
Total	$390.75	$366.75

Table 1. — *Yield and stumpage value of timber cut and annual yield and value of nuts, per acre, in planted black walnut stand (Case A), site index 70*[1]

Age (years)	Trees	Mean tree diameter	Volume cut[2]	Stumpage price per M bd. ft.	Stumpage value of trees cut	Annual nut yield[3]	Value of nuts[4]
	No.	Inches	M bd. ft.	Dollars	Dollars	Pounds	Dollars
10	135	4.9	--	--	--	--	--
15	135	6.8	—	--	--	392	20
20	135	8.3	--	--	--	1,336	67
25	135	10.0	0.15	97	15	1,958	98
30	120	11.9	.45	98	44	2,472	124
35	95	13.5	.62	104	64	2,508	125
40	74	15.2	.64	108	69	2,462	123
45	60	16.8	.68	352	239	2,280	114
50	50	18.4	.92	386	355	2,245	112
55	40	20.0	.98	525	514	2,100	105
60	32	21.6	.65	626	407	1,840	92
65	28	23.3	.40	750	300	1,750	88
70	26	24.9	.47	808	380	1,809	90
75	24	26.5	.54	1,530	826	1,843	92
80	22	28.1	7.10	1,655	11,750	1,841	92

[1] Adapted from Naughton (1970). Figures rounded.
[2] Volume of intermediate cut at age shown. Entire stand cut at age 80.
[3] Average yield for age shown and previous 4 years.
[4] Gross revenue at 5 cents per pound.

Vegetation control was repeated in the second and third years. The cost of pruning walnut stems was $0.50 per tree, based on a study in Kansas by Clark (1953). This resulted in costs of $67.50 for Case A and $13.00 for Case B, each occurring three times. Annual costs consist of real property taxes, $3.00 per acre and $7.00 to cover items such as inspection, control of pests, and fence maintenance. The taxes, higher than present-day levels for farm land in Missouri, anticipate continued increases. Costs associated with growing fescue seed are accounted for under revenues, which are net.

REVENUES

Grade yields of timber stumpage sold are those reported by Naughton (1970), which included grades designated prime, select, and common. Trees 10 to 12 inches in d.b.h. produced 25 percent select and 75 percent common. The percentage of select increased with tree size. Trees 17 inches in diameter included 20 percent prime, 25 percent select, and 55 percent common. The proportion of prime increased with tree size, and the harvest cut was distributed 50, 30, and 20 percent respectively for prime, select, and common.

Unit prices for stumpage also were adapted from Naughton (1970). For the purpose of assigning value, the diameter inside bark of the tree 17 feet above ground level was taken as the average log diameter of the tree. The resulting unit rates show that trees 10 to 15 inches in diameter were valued at about $100 per M board feet (table 1). Because of higher quality associated with larger tree size, the stumpage value of trees cut increased rapidly from $240 for 17-inch trees to $380 for 25-inch trees. Larger trees contained substantially more veneer quality material and prices exceed $1,500 per M board feet. These stumpage rates appear to be high, but if the demand for walnut logs continues, future prices may well equal or surpass these levels.

The cost of selling timber stumpage was set at $5 per M board feet sold. It includes the costs of negotiating sales, contract preparation, and supervision. Income taxes are difficult to estimate without knowledge of a specific taxpayer's income, deductible items, and the applicable tax rate. However, an informal study of 30 timber stumpage sales indicated that the seller paid income taxes amounting to 15 percent of gross revenue. Revenue was reduced by selling costs and depletion allowances and the remainder was eligible for classification as a long-term capital gain. Accordingly income taxes were set at 15 percent of gross revenue.

Revenue from nuts under Case A is shown in table 1. Nut revenues for Case B were 10 percent higher, reflecting higher nut yields. These are based on a delivered price of 5 cents per pound. In the analysis, one-third was deducted to provide for the cost of collection and hauling (Whitney and Porterfield 1967). Net annual returns from sale of fescue seed were based on trials in southwest Missouri. For Case A the annual revenue was $37.50 per acre and for Case B $75.00. Whether these levels can be achieved and maintained is not known. Income taxes on revenue from nuts and fescue seed was set at 25 percent of the revenue.

ANALYSIS

Criteria used for evaluation were discounted net worth (DNW), internal rate of return (IRR) and benefit-cost ratio (B/C). DNW results from discounting all costs and returns to the year in which the investment was undertaken at a selected rate of interest (discount). The larger the rate of discount, which is a measure of the value of elapsed time, the lower the DNW. IRR is the discount rate at which the sum of discounted costs equals the sum of discounted revenues; that is, DNW is zero. It is the prospective rate of return that the investment would earn when adjusted for time. The B/C ratio indicates the number of dollars of revenue that would be received for each dollar of cost incurred when these elements are discounted at a selected rate.

Using the costs and revenues previously described, the results were determined. To save time, calculations were done by electronic computer utilizing the program RETURN, prepared by Schweitzer et al. (1967), and the results summarized (table 2).

Case B, open-grown walnut trees at a 40- by 40-foot spacing without thinning, appears to be a more attractive investment alternative. The DNW estimates at several rates of discount are higher for Case B. The DNW of $618 computed at 6 percent, for example, may be interpreted to mean that the investment returned $618 per acre in excess of a 6 percent return. Or, an additional $618 could have been incurred initially and the rate of return would be 6 percent. For Case A, the DNW of minus $122 indicates that the venture failed to earn 10 percent. If initial expenses, for example, could be reduced by $122, a rate of 10 percent would be earned.

The IRR estimates require no arbitrary selection of a guiding rate of return. They indicate that if all quantities, prices, and other elements were to actually occur, Case A would earn an annual equivalent rate of return of 8.3

Table 2. — *Investment returns for two different spacings of walnut according to three criteria*

Case	Discounted net worth, percent				Internal rate of return	Benefit-cost ratio at 6 percent
	4	6	8	10		
	Dollars	Dollars	Dollars	Dollars	Percent	
Case A[1]	1,376	378	29	-122	8.3	1.39
Case B[2]	1,517	618	284	125	12.9	1.67

[1] Spacing 18 by 18 feet, 135 trees per acre.
[2] Spacing 40 by 40 feet, 26 trees per acre.

percent and Case B would earn 12.9 percent. The B/C ratios, based on a discount rate of 6 percent, indicate that Case A would return 1.39 dollars in revenue for each dollar of cost incurred and Case B would return 1.67. At higher rates of discount the B/C ratios would become progressively smaller and would reach 1.00 when computed at 8.3 percent for Case A and 12.9 percent for Case B.

When all revenues and all costs are summed for the 80-year period, they are not greatly different for Case A and for Case B, although the individual costs and revenues differ to some extent (table 3). When discounted at 6 percent, the annual incomes from nuts and fescue seed assume greater importance. It is significant that the timber revenues, which are received at the end of the production period, are extremely small in terms of present or discounted value. As to costs, initial investment and income taxes comprise a large share of the totals.

A potential investor would be interested in the size of initial investment required for a 40-acre plantation. For Case A the cost of land, site preparation, fertilizer, fencing, planting walnut, and sowing fescue would be approximately $16,000. For Case B, because fewer trees were planted, the cost would be $15,000.

DISCUSSION

The contribution of annual or frequently occurring revenues has a large bearing on investment outcome. This indicates the desirability of planning a multiple-crop enterprise. The investor should take advantage of research and technology that will increase net revenues from nuts and interplanted farm crops. Initial investment and annually recurring expenses, if held as low as possible without detracting from yields, can materially increase net returns. If genetic research can develop faster-growing black walnut trees, shorter rotations will be possible, which should increase profitability.

Table 3. — *Total and discounted (6 percent) revenues and costs per acre for two different spacings of walnut over an 80-year period*

Item	Total				Discounted at 6 percent			
	Case A		Case B		Case A		Case B	
	Dollars	Percent	Dollars	Percent	Dollars	Percent	Dollars	Percent
Revenue:								
Fescue seed	3,000	13	6,000	26	619	47	1,238	80
Nuts	4,468	20	2,824	12	483	36	168	11
Timber	14,897	66	13,844	61	228	17	131	9
Return of land value	200	1	200	1	2	0*	2	0*
Total	22,565	100	22,868	100	1,332	100	1,539	100
Cost:								
Initial, including land	391	7	367	7	391	41	367	40
Annual expense	800	14	800	15	165	17	165	18
Income taxes	4,112	75	4,289	78	302	32	371	40
Pruning, weed control	214	4	19	0*	96	10	19	2
Total	5,517	100	5,475	100	954	100	922	100

[1] Spacing 18 by 18 feet, 135 trees per acre.
[2] Spacing 40 by 40 feet, 26 trees per acre.
* Less than 0.5.

An analysis of this nature has a number of shortcomings. Adequately documented information on yields, costs, and returns usually is lacking so the "best" estimates available are used. Unforeseen losses may occur and catastrophic events happen all too frequently. Nevertheless, an investor should use all means possible to appraise a potential investment in black walnut.

LITERATURE CITED

Clark, F. Bryan. 1953. Time required to prune black walnut trees. USDA For. Serv. Cent. States For. Exp. Stn., Stn. Note 78.

Krajicek, John E., and Robert D. Williams. 1971. Continuing weed control benefits young planted black walnut. USDA For. Serv. Res. Note NC-122, 3 p. North Cent. For. Exp. Stn., St. Paul, Minn.

Naughton, Gary G. 1970. Growth and yield of black walnut plantations. Coop. Ext. Serv., Kans. State Univ.

Schweitzer, Dennis L., Allen L. Lundgren, and Robert F. Wambach. 1967. A computer program for evaluating long-term forestry investments. USDA For. Serv. Res. Pap. NC-10, 34 p., illus. North Cent. For. Exp. Stn., St. Paul, Minn.

Whitney, R. W., and J. G. Porterfield. 1967. Pecan harvester development at O.S.U. North. Nut Grow. Assoc. 58th Annu. Rep. p. 68-74.

INFORMATION AND SERVICES AVAILABLE
TO THE LANDOWNER

Burl S. Ashley, *Field Representative*
USDA Forest Service, State and Private Forestry
Forestry Sciences Laboratory, Southern Illinois University
Carbondale, Illinois
and
John P. Slusher, *Extension Forester*
School of Forestry, University of Missouri
Columbia, Missouri

ABSTRACT.—The efficient production and marketing of walnut products is dependent upon aid available to the grower. Many sources and kinds of aid exist including on-the-ground technical assistance, publications, seminars, and incentive payments. By carefully analyzing his needs and soliciting assistance from the proper source, each grower can better prepare himself for a successful walnut enterprise.

The subject of black walnut has received more attention within the last 10 years than ever before. Researchers have been delving into the "world of walnut" with increasing fervor which has unlocked many of the secrets to growing and utilizing this valuable species. In addition, landowners have become increasingly aware of the benefits derived from growing walnut and are seeking knowledge to make their growing and marketing operations more efficient and profitable.

Scientists are interested in getting their research applied. On the other hand, landowners desire to learn more about this research and put it into use. These two segments of the "walnut enterprise" must be closely associated if full success is to be achieved. There are many connecting links which, if properly used, will serve to fulfill the needs of numerous individuals involved with the growing and marketing of walnut products. These links include on-the-ground technical assistance, publications, seminars and other informational meetings, a multiplicity of sources for general information and incentives programs.

ON-THE-GROUND
TECHNICAL ASSISTANCE

The walnut grower who desires guidance with plantation establishment, insect and disease control, thinning,

pruning, or other aspects of management and marketing has various sources for these services.

All States within the commercial range of black walnut provide services, usually free, to private landowners who have forestry problems, such as the growing and marketing of walnut trees. These services are provided under the Cooperative Forest Management (CFM) Act of 1950, the legal basis for a cooperative effort between the USDA Forest Service and the State forestry organization. Upon request, arrangements can be made for a visit from a State-employed forester who will give professional guidance to the landowner. These foresters are referred to by various titles in different States. For example, in Missouri they are called farm foresters, in Illinois they are called district foresters, and in Indiana they are called service foresters. These men can be located by contacting any local government agriculture office or the State forester who is usually located in the State's capital city. These foresters provide advice about most aspects of producing walnut products from planting to the marketing and utilization of the final product.

Often a landowner desires to grow walnut but prefers not to do it himself. In such cases he will need a competent individual to manage the enterprise for him. A consulting forester can be the answer. These foresters are self-employed and offer their professional services to the public for a fee. Though consulting foresters are relatively few in number, State forestry employees know where they may be easily contacted by landowners. Consulting foresters perform most of the same services as the State-employed foresters, but also offer additional assistance. For instance, in the case of plantation establishment, the State-employed forester prepares a plan, whereas the consulting forester not only prepares a plan, but carries it out. In the field of marketing, the consulting forester will carry out the entire sales operation while his State-employed counterpart is usually limited to tree selection and marking, supplying a list of buyers, assisting with the preparation of a contract, and other general duties.

Since soil conditions are critically important in a walnut-growing enterprise, a grower should always have an analysis made of the site. Some data may be obtained by the inspecting forester or by submitting soil samples to the local Cooperative Extension Service Office. However, a more detailed analysis is provided through the local soil and water conservation districts cooperating with the Soil Conservation Service of the U.S. Department of Agriculture. They usually have an office in each county. A visit or call to one of these offices will provide information concerning the availability of a soils analysis. Some soil and water conservation districts also offer tree planting services. All districts make recommendations regarding erosion control and conservation measures needed for each soil type involved.

Some private nurseries offer plantation establishment services including site preparation, planting stock, planting, and weed control. These nurseries are limited in number; however, they can be located by contacting a local forester.

PUBLICATIONS

Regardless of the amount of professional services the landowner secures, it is important that he brief himself regarding walnut. Much of this familiarization should be done while he is contemplating his walnut management activities and certainly he should keep himself up to date as he proceeds with the work. An excellent approach to building a broad comprehensive background of knowledge on the subject is to secure good publications. These publications are available from several sources. Since it is impossible to list all

of them, only the principal sources are contained in the following list:

1. *Cooperative Extension Service.*
    a. Local offices — usually one in each county (normally at the county seat).
    b. Extension forester — located at the State university.
2. *State Forestry Division.*
    a. Local offices — check at agriculture offices for location.
    b. State forester at headquarters office.
3. *Soil Conservation Service.* Most counties have an office located at the county seat.
4. *United Hardwood Forestry Program,* Attention: Mr. Larry Frye, Columbia City, Indiana.
5. *North Central Forest Experiment Station,* USDA Forest Service, Folwell Avenue, St. Paul, Minnesota 55101, or Forestry Sciences Laboratory, Southern Illinois University, Carbondale, Illinois 62901. A bibliography of many walnut publications is also available from this source.
6. *State and Private Forestry, USDA Forest Service,* 6816 Market Street, Upper Darby, Pennsylvania 19082, or Forestry Sciences Laboratory, Southern Illinois University, Carbondale, Illinois 62901.

SEMINARS

Since the demand for information on walnut has increased, there not only has been an influx of increased services and publications, but several walnut seminars have been conducted to augment these other sources of assistance. Basically, these seminars are of two kinds — one type is for professional foresters organized by State forestry divisions or the Cooperative Extension Service, and the other is designed for the general public organized by the Cooperative Extension Service. Several seminars have been sponsored by the walnut industries. Those presenting information have included walnut growers, the Cooperative Extension Service, USDA Forest Service, Soil Conservation Service, State forestry organizations, universities, walnut industries, and others.

Seminars are not presented at any prescribed interval but only when there is sufficient demand within a geographic area and the sponsoring agency considers one feasible. Landowners may request such seminars through local Cooperative Extension Offices, local foresters, or by contacting the State offices mentioned in the preceding paragraphs.

ADDITIONAL SOURCES OF INFORMATION

Many sources provide valuable information, even though their primary function is not assisting walnut growers. In some instances these sources have information on specific subjects which is of value. Following is a partial list of these sources:

1. Walnut Council, USDA Forest Service, Forestry Sciences Laboratory, Southern Illinois University, Carbondale, Illinois 62901. This organization will refer requests for assistance or information to a competent source. Members are periodically informed of the latest developments concerning walnut.

2. Northern Nutgrowers Association, 4518 Holston Hills Road, Knoxville, Tennessee 37914. Members are kept informed about the production of nuts.

3. Local or State Nutgrowers Associations. Several States have such associations. The State offices of the various service organizations can usually advise as to the availability of local nutgrowers associations. Information is available to members through meetings and newsletters.

4. Fine Hardwoods – American Walnut Association, 666 North Shore Drive, Chicago, Illinois 60611. Requests for information regarding walnut will be referred to an appropriate source of assistance.

5. Wood-Using Industries. Many large veneer log and saw log industries are willing to give information to a grower or advise him of where he can secure assistance.

6. American Forestry Institute, 1619 Massachusetts Avenue, NW, Washington, D.C. 20036. This organization occasionally prepares information on walnut and gives assistance and support to walnut programs. It sponsors the American Tree Farm System and welcomes walnut growers to participate in this program and receive recognition for their contribution to forestry.

7. Nut-Using Industries. Information is offered concerning the marketing of nuts. In addition, they sometimes have programs involving the growing of nuts and are willing to offer assistance.

8. Other Growers. Valuable information and assistance are available from other experienced walnut growers.

INCENTIVE PAYMENTS

The Rural Environmental Assistance Program (REAP), which is administered by the Agricultural Conservation and Stabilization Service (ASCS), provides incentive payments for approved walnut plantings and cultural practices. The payments are usually 75 to 80 percent of the overall cost. This U.S. Department of Agriculture program is financed with a limited amount of funds in each county. Because these funds are divided among many agricultural practices, the amount available for forestry purposes is small. Approval must be received before a project is initiated. If a walnut grower is interested in the REAP, he should contact the ASCS office in the county where he will perform the practice.

PESTICIDE PRECAUTIONARY STATEMENT

Pesticides used improperly can be injurious to man, animals, and plants. Follow the directions and heed all precautions on the labels.

Store pesticides in original containers under lock and key — out of the reach of children and animals — and away from food and feed.

Apply pesticides so that they do not endanger humans, livestock, crops, beneficial insects, fish, and wildlife. Do not apply pesticides when there is danger of drift, when honey bees or other pollinating insects are visiting plants, or in ways that may contaminate water or leave illegal residues.

Avoid prolonged inhalation of pesticide sprays or dusts; wear protective clothing and equipment if specified on the container.

If your hands become contaminated with a pesticide, do not eat or drink until you have washed. In case a pesticide is swallowed or gets in the eyes, follow the first aid treatment given on the label, and get prompt medical attention. If a pesticide is spilled on your skin or clothing, remove clothing immediately and wash skin thoroughly.

Do not clean spray equipment or dump excess spray material near ponds, streams, or wells. Because it is difficult to remove all traces of herbicides from equipment, do not use the same equipment for insecticides or fungicides that you use for herbicides.

Dispose of empty pesticide containers promptly. Have them buried at a sanitary land-fill dump, or crush and bury them in a level, isolated place.

NOTE: Some States have restrictions on the use of certain pesticides. Check your State and local regulations. Also, because registrations of pesticides are under constant review by the U.S. Department of Agriculture, consult your county agricultural agent or State Extension specialist to be sure the intended use is still registered.

CPSIA information can be obtained at www.ICGtesting.com
Printed in the USA
BVOW06s1800121114

374746BV00002B/42/P